T3-BSC-788

N A R R O W   I S   T H E   W A Y

BY

SERGEI SAZONOV

Victor Press
P.O. Box 23021
Los Angeles, California

Library of Congress Catalog Card Number 70-136365

To my wife - on our 25th Anniversary

I

"They, who were returned to homes, never, have never, talked to anyone about their life in Siberia because it was forbidden to them, but people knew very much about Siberia's camps since the days of the Czarist Russia...."

It was not yet ten o'clock but the room was dimly lit by the fading white Northern lights. Over and over again as I paced up and down the room, I repeated the text of Stalin's Constitution. Article 127: "Citizens of the U.S.S.R. are guaranteed inviolability of the person. No person may be placed under arrest except by decision of a court or with the sanction of a procurate." Article 128: "The inviolability of the homes of citizens and privacy of correspondence are protected by law."

I must learn the whole constitution, many pages; I must nail it in my mind, pound it in so I would not fail the last high school examinations—I had to enter the university in the fall. My whole future depended on it. Without a university education the best I could hope for was to become a common laborer.

"Sergei," I heard my mother say, "you have studied long enough. Stop now. The samovar is singing. I'll make tea."

I turned, and I shall never forget her as she sat by the window calmly sewing. She was a fine little woman, with great dark eyes, and her thick, brown hair was drawn back in a tight knot. My mother was a kindergarten teacher who did dressmaking in the evenings to help keep our small home together and send me to school. My brother was in the army. She half rose from her chair when suddenly there was a loud knock at the door and before Mother had time to say "Come in" two uniformed men shouldered their way in.

"Tovarich* Sasonova?" asked the sergeant looking at Mother.

---

*Comrade

Mother stood, staring, her face drained of all color, but she managed to say in almost a whisper, "Yes, I am."

"Your son?"

"Yes."

"Show me your identification cards," he commanded, and we handed over our cards.

"You two will come with us. Pack what you can. You may take twenty kilograms each. Be quick about it."

"But where? Why?" I asked of him, wondering what this was about.

"Please, Sergei, don't talk," whispered Mother and in that moment I noticed the raspberry color in the Sergeant's insignia. This raspberry color is worn by the N.K.V.D., the Russian Secret Police. It means only three things: prison, death or Siberia. My thoughts screamed, "Oh no! It can't be. It can't happen to us. It is impossible. There is some mistake, surely!" In that terrible moment my mind seemed to leave my body.

Once before uniformed men had come to our home. But that was a long time ago when they came to tell us about my father. They told us where he was and we found him, a white, shrunken man in a hospital bed. Two days later they told Mother he had died.

But why did they want us, my mother and me? What had we done? Of what were we guilty? There must be some mistake—

"But are you sure --- ?" I began.

The shorter man stood rigidly, his index finger imperatively jabbing. "Shut up, you!"

In my hand I still held the book, "Stalin's Constitution." I moved forward showing this to the Sergeant and saying, "You can't arrest us for anything. We are law-abiding Soviet citizens and the law says you have no right to do anything without --- "

"I'll show you my right and my law," he interrupted and took a step nearer to me with uplifted hand.

"No, no," screamed my mother as she jumped in front of me; but the man struck twice and we both fell to the floor. As I struggled to get up my mother held me with both hands.

"No, Sergie, no. I beg you, be careful. They will kill you," she whispered.

I saw the blood on her mouth and I saw the cruel face of the Sergeant, and I said to myself, "This face I will never forget, never, never! God in heaven, why am I so helpless? Why can't I protect my mother from these brutes? What is happening to me, to my mother? Where is the law? Where are the proud words of Stalin's

Constitution?"

I helped Mother to her feet and after she bathed the blood from her face, we started to pack our luggage.

Surprised, I saw the prepared food she immediately brought out. Packages of cheese, smoked sausage, tea and bread. "Please wrap them, Son," she said softly.

"But, Momotchka -- "

"Hush, Son. Tie the packages." She thrust a heavy cord in my hand.

Numbly I thought of the friends who had silently disappeared in the last few weeks, friends never heard from again, and on the locked doors of their homes, the government seal told all. Mother and I talked about these friends many times while she sewed money in our clothes. I had secretly laughed at her; this could happen to others, yes, but not us. Or so I thought in the spring of 1941 when I was seventeen.

By the door I stopped a little and looked back at our home... would I ever see it again? The Sergeant sealed up the door and took the keys from Mother. There behind the locked door, the book, "Stalin's Constitution," lay on the floor, smeared with the blood of my mother.

II

Wearing our heavy winter coats, even though this was June, we were marched down the stairs, I carrying both blanket-wrapped bundles. In the street we were loaded into a huge truck as though we were cattle. The conveyance was nearly full of other captives, but we managed to crowd in and, sitting on our luggage, we were rocked back and forth. We were driven many miles. Not a word was spoken.

About midnight we were ordered out into a scene I shall never forget. Huge overhead lights made everything bright as day. Here, too, all was quiet. The only voices heard were those of the guards as they sternly ordered the people out of the trucks and into a waiting cattle train. As soon as a truck drove in and discharged its human cargo, another truck repeated the cycle.

The guards seemed to know their work perfectly. They stood watching the lines of people walk slowly with bent heads. Some sobbed silently. They carried bundles wrapped in blankets or coats, tied with rope or string, anything they could find in their hurry and fright.

Mothers with babies in their arms and small children tugging at their skirts were directed up the steep ramps. Those whose husbands were there to assist them were lucky.

A few of the smaller children, snatched out of their beds in the night, cried a little but were hushed by their mothers at once. Children and even babies seemed to know by instinct that they must obey; they must not cry. Only their big wide eyes told of the uncertainty they felt.

I glanced at Mother as she stood beside me, but she just looked at me and shook her head as if in disbelief at what she saw. After a short wait we were told to go to one of the old, dirty cattle cars. There were no windows, but a few boards had been ripped out near the roof. A wide door yawned before me with a crude ramp leading up to it. There was nothing to do but go up that ramp leading to the car. I looked around for Mother, and found her helping a young woman with her little children. I picked up our bundles and walked up.

The car had been fitted with bunks, or shelves if you will, three tiers high and about two and a half feet wide. I secured the middle bunk for Mother and a top one for myself, and became part of the confusion of trying to fit our belongings into a narrow space that was to be our home. For how long, we had no idea.

More people came with bundles and frightened children. Men swore under their breath. Swearing or complaining out loud would have brought the clubs of the guards down on them. All these frightened fragments of humanity climbed the steep ramp until the car was packed with terror-stricken souls.

There were signs that the car had recently been used for cattle and the barnyard smell was everywhere. To city-born and bred people, this was nauseating. I did what I could to clean the floor.

It was not long before the children were asleep; and the adults settled down to what, under normal circumstances, would have been a quiet evening. No one spoke, each afraid that next to him might be a spy. We knew Stalin's men were spying everywhere and certainly this place could be no exception. A profound silence settled over the car.

I stood by myself in the only home I had now, and surveyed the people who were to be my companions on this strange journey. I noticed Mother nod briefly to three or four women and I recognized them as neighbors. Then I knew why Mother had been able to bring out food and blankets and clothes so quickly at the guard's command. I had wondered how so much new strong rope just happened to be in our apartment. She and the neighbors had been talking and suspecting such a trip as this! Yes, and the money Mother had sewn in my clothes! Subconsciously I reached to see if it was still there.

Dear, thoughtful Momotchka! Now here she was in this horrible terrifying position. Suddenly I felt my responsibility to her. She was all I had and I was all she had.

But what could I do? I looked at the forty or fifty people in the car sitting on the edge of bunks or on the floor. Silent they were. Their eyes stared wide with fright. Now and again someone whispered and more than once, adding to the unspeakable gloom, I heard the word **Siberia.** They all knew. Suddenly the full impact of my position dawned on me. I was one of them! We were all bound for the same place: Siberia, prison, or hard labor in camps, maybe for life. But what could I do for Mother or for those miserable creatures? I was as helpless as they, facing the prospect of a living death in an abominable place.

I turned and stood by the open door near the armed guard and watched more victims being shunted into the cars.

At last the door was closed and locked from the outside, and the train started. It was not yet morning. Everyone climbed into his bunk and pretended to sleep.

III

But there was no sleep for me as I lay on my less than three-foot shelf, which was too narrow and too short. The boards were rough and there was no mattress. I had only one blanket. This I tried to give to my mother, but she would not hear of it.

"No, I have my own and I may as well get used to it. Your young health needs more care than mine does. Keep the blanket--"

"But, Mother --- " I interrupted.

"Obey me, Son," in her sternest voice was her only answer.

All I could think of as the train pounded over the rough tracks was Siberia. The flat wheel on the car made a dull monotonous sound, and as it slapped with each revolution it seemed to say Siberia, Siberia, Siberia. Every word I had ever heard about the place came to mind, and each one of them brought another picture of the dreadul life there.

I had read about the slave labor during the Czar's time; then as now, convicts worked underground in mines—salt, gold, coal and everything else the country provided; also a great deal of work was carried on in the forests, felling and sawing trees. It was general knowledge that prisoners were forced to work out their lives, existing under the most primitive conditions. Once in awhile someone would return to civilization. Even though the prisoners were forbidden to communicate with the outside world, a few words trickled through. I learned the prisoners were not guarded very rigorously. It was not necessary as the camps were always located deep in the forests or in Siberia's Steppes and very far from roads or settlements. The great distances, deep snows, extreme cold, wild animals and other natural obstacles served to guard the prisoners even more than the human guards. If anyone had such luck as to get away to the railroad and get on a train, his heart full of hope of freedom, he would surely be arrested, because the train guards identified every passenger.

After the revolution of 1917, prisoners also worked on building power stations, factories and even whole cities. But work in mines was still the most common job for the slaves.

All these things ran through my mind as I lay on my shelf. I couldn't make myself believe Mother and I could be on such a trip. It just could not be happening. I felt sure I would open my eyes and find it all a terrible dream.

With the coming of dawn the train was moving very fast. It seemed they wanted to get us out of the city as rapidly as possible. All was quiet in the car, except for a few snores of the sleepers. There must have been others as wide awake as I was, but they lay silently as me.

IV

When morning finally dawned, everyone started to climb down out of his berth, or bunk, or shelf, and began to look around for something to eat. Very little was said aloud, although I could hear whispers everywhere. When the train slowed to a stop, several climbed into the top bunks to peek out where the boards had been removed for air. From where I lay I could see we were out in the country. Just after the train stopped the door was unlocked from the outside and we saw a guard there—that despicable guard who had stood at the foot of the ramp driving the human cattle into the car, demanding more and more speed as each man or woman struggled with his baggage and little children. How I hated that man! Everyone tried to talk at once, asking questions, but he said not a word. He just stood there, feet spread apart, one hand on the gun strapped in his holster.

Finally he held up his hand for silence. "You all want to know where you are, where you are going and why. I can't tell you, because if you don't know, how could I know? And now if you'll shut up long enough I'll tell you where you can get something to eat. Just two cars ahead is the kitchen car. The train will stop long enough for all to go there for breakfast and later for dinner. Those of you who brought food can stay here and eat it if you want to. That is all."

Questions were hurled at him from all directions but he answered only, "I don't know. I've told you I don't know. I don't know, damn you. I have only my orders. If you want anything to eat, you had better get over to the kitchen."

After the guard left there was a great scramble for breakfast. We found our way to the kitchen car and after waiting our turn, received tea and black bread. After this very unsatisfactory meal, we went back to our car. There was a great deal of carefully guarded conversation, but I noticed Mother did not take part in it. There was nothing for us to do. We were helpless, just as the cattle had been that had formerly ridden in this car.

Later in the day cabbage soup and black bread was handed out as the main meal of the day. Mother and I supplemented this with cheese and sausage. Mother missed her samovar.

"There is so much comfort in a cup of steaming hot tea made right from the samovar, but . . . "

"Yes, Mother, I know. I'd have been glad to carry it, but if I had, we'd have had to leave the food. You know it is heavy."

"Yes, Son, I know," she sighed.

V

My parents had always lived in Leningrad. My father was born in 1890, a musician by profession, playing clarinet in many large orchestras, theatre, symphonies and the world-renowned Russian circus. He died in 1932 leaving Mother with two sons: Aleksey, fifteen and I, eight. From my scant memory of my father, he was tall with dark hair and eyes. Aleksey and I both resemble my father. Mother was born in 1894. I remember her as always quiet and reserved, and in an emergency her face muscles would tighten but she always remained calm until after the difficulty had passed, when she would explain all to me, at least all she thought I should know. When she was alone in her room, thinking I did not know, she was often tearful.

While Father lived Mother gave all of her time and thought to her home and family. After Father's death she secured a position teaching in a kindergarten. Then her system of housekeeping changed. Aleksey and I did most of the marketing and I marveled at the patience Mother must have been exercising all these years. I found she had been going from one market to another to find just the plainest kind of food. There was never enough of anything in the stores and often I came home empty handed or with the strangest kinds of substitutes. The markets couldn't supply the demand and this was the way with everything we tried to buy. The favored Communist bureaucracy, the new Russian nobility, bought their supplies from special privileged stores. I was never in one of those stores; the ration card I carried wouldn't get me past the door.

When Aleksey graduated from the gymnasium, he wanted to go to the university; but the need in the home was so great and Mother was so tired all the time, that he decided against it. Going out in the world to work he assumed the role as head of the family. This was much easier on Mother and things went well until Aleksey was drafted in 1939. We had only one letter from him. Then Mother began to do dressmaking in the evenings to help financially. I wanted to quit school and go to work but Mother would not hear of it.

"Your father was an educated man and I know he'd want you to be the same. Never you mind, dear, we'll get along."

"But, Mother -- "

"My son, you have always obeyed me without question, and I expect you to do the same now," and she went on with her sewing.

It now fell on me to saw and chop all the firewood for our heat. Aleksey had taught me so well that soon it was no burden and I even sawed and chopped wood for the neighbors and in this way I felt I was earning at least part of my keep. Mother appreciated my efforts.

Over the years I had often asked Mother about the circumstances of my father's death. One time Aleksey overheard Mother say, "Sergei, dear, you must not ask, because I can't tell you. He is gone from us and that is all I can say. I've told you this before, Son, and the answer must always be the same."

"But, Mother -- "

Aleksey looked up from his book. "Look here, brother, Mother has told you. Don't ever ask that question again. If you do, I'll beat you very hard, and I mean **very hard**. Our father is dead. He is gone. Don't ever ask again. Remember what I said." With that he went back to his book and Mother walked out to the kitchen. It was left in doubt, a doubt which never left me. Why? Why? Why?

Mother tried to educate me in the spirit of religion but the negative influence of school and of society in general was much stronger and I grew up an atheist.

At school we were taught the Darwin theory and the doctrine of Karl Marx. We were told our parents were too old to understand this new regime but we must do our best to teach them. The teachers told us that religion was invented by rich men and capitalists in order to keep the workers and poor people in obedience and subjection. Religion taught that everyone must obey the Czar because he was chosen by God to rule the people. It also taught non-violence so that people wouldn't stir up a revolution against the capitalists. We were taught the priests were servants of the capitalists who deluded the people every day; that they were really our worst enemies. Religion was nothing but an anesthetic for the people because there was no God.

I tried to talk with Mother to explain there was no God, but she remained silent; listening, but always at the end of an evening of a one-sided conversation she would sigh and shake her head.

Even though our conversations invariably ended up this way, I never gave up; the pressure at school was too great. But I felt I was right and what I learned at school was the only answer, in spite of Mother's sighing and shaking her head.

I would forget all about Mother at school as I listened to a lecture that U.S.S.R. and Stalin were fighting to save Russia from capitalism and slavery and that things were not as they should be because of the way the Czar had run the country; but soon everything would be right, better than ever and U.S.S.R. would be strong and all would be happy.

One day, when I got home from school, I found the walls bare, stripped of the religious emblems and holy pictures which had been there ever since I could remember. I practically jumped for joy.

"Oh, Momotchka, you see it at last. You've taken them down! I can go to school tomorrow and tell all. This will be a great credit to me."

Mother said not a word but sat down in her favorite chair and gazed out the window, her face set in the stern lines I had been noticing lately.

Indeed it was a victory for me at school the next day. I was hailed as a hero and introduced as such to my class. My elation was short lived, however, for when I got home that day Mother was sewing furiously at her machine. She spoke to me very little. When she wasn't sewing, she gazed out at nothing. She continued to be so sad I couldn't bear it. One evening I cried out to her, "Momotchka, put them back. The home is not the same. I'm lonely without them. The walls are bare and I can't fall asleep. Put them back, please, Momotchka!"

"No, Son, it is better this way." That was all she said and went on with her sewing.

"Where are they? I'll put them back myself. I can't stand these lonely walls and your sad face any longer." I dashed for Mother's large chest where she kept her treasures. It was locked. "Give me the key, Momotchka, please," I begged.

"Here is the key but the icons and pictures are not there. See for yourself."

My search revealed nothing and Mother continued to repeat, "It is better this way."

"But why, Mother? Why don't you let me put them back?"

"Listen to me, Son. You are too young to understand these things. When you grow up I'll explain everything to you, my darling," she said very gently. "But now, my little boy, promise me something, will you?"

I nodded my head. "Yes, Momotchka, I will. What is it?"

"It will be our secret, Son. If anyone, I mean anyone in the world, ever asks you if your mother attends church, or prays, or believes in God, you must say 'No, she doesn't attend church; she doesn't believe in God.' The reason is if anyone knew I attended church or believed in God, I would lose my position. Teachers are not supposed to believe in God. And do you know I think that I don't believe in God any more? It is only a habit now, praying and going to church."

I saw that she wasn't telling the truth and I was sad to see my mother's face as she forced herself to tell these lies. Feeling uneasy, I looked at the floor.

"You wouldn't want me to lose my position. How would we live?" she continued. "As a worker I couldn't earn enough to support us and keep you and your brother in school. So it is agreed? This is going to be our little secret, all right?"

"Yes," I answered, without enthusiasm, and the praise I had received in school faded away. I could not understand why my mother must not believe in God as long as she didn't bring harm to anyone.

All this left me in a state of confusion. With the holy icons gone we were, to all appearances, a non-believing family, but I knew Mother continued to pray. I was confused as to who I was. According to my school I was an atheist; but at home I was a doubting son of a Christian. I never again talked to Mother about atheistic Communism.

VI

There had been very little noise or confusion before the train started. Everyone was afraid to complain or even to talk in front of the guards. But when the whistle blew and the train began to move, the car was filled with loud wails and cries from the victims as though only at that moment did they realize they might soon die. An older man's remark, "People live in Siberia too," was met with more howls.

The train rapidly picked up speed, getting us away from the city as fast as possible. After we were safely away from Leningrad, the train slowed down and by the time we reached the Ural Mountains we were barely crawling. When the train stopped overnight in the middle of the plain where no one could possibly have escaped, we were allowed out for a little rest.

We dragged on toward the east with many stops along the way. The guards slackened their vigilance as no one could get away anyway, so far out in the empty spaces we were without identification cards.

Sometimes the train stopped at a small town where we were permitted to buy food from the peasants who brought food to the train. Those of us who had a little money were glad of this as the food in the kitchen car was very poor.

The families in our car tried to be congenial; the older men talked; the women cared for the children and gossiped, but always in whispers. The fear of saying the wrong word was ever present. The feeling of terror never left us. The younger group, my age, grew tired of playing cards to while away the dreary hours. There were a few girls about sixteen or eighteen years old, but we were so crowded there was no opportunity for romance. I had never been seriously interested in girls, always shy of them, and my studies kept me so busy I had no time for romance. On this miserable, slow, dirty, crawling train I could think only of the future, but with nothing concrete on which to pin my thoughts.

There were two doctors on the train but they were prisoners like the rest of us. When their medicines and supplies were exhausted they had no way of getting more. Several babies were born on the train, one of them in our car. Both doctors were busy in other cars, so the women had to deliver the baby and care for the mother. There was no happiness or celebration at the birth of a baby as each new life meant only more anxiety.

There were four deaths during the trip. If the person had the luck to die near a place where there was a cemetery, the burial was made there; but if we were passing through open country at the time of death, the train was stopped and a grave was dug in a field near the railroad track. I helped dig one such grave.

No priests were on the train—they had been shipped to Siberia long before—so some older man recited a prayer over the dead and someone else whittled out a cross of wood. People stood waiting for the corpse to be carried out. Then everyone followed as the dead with its cross was carried to its final resting place—a lonely grave far from home. I would hear a melancholy Russian song all through the dreary miserable night after each burial, as the train moved on across the endless Siberian plain.

VII

One morning in the latter part of June, the car door opened and the guard climbed in. He stood, hands on hips, feet spread far apart, and looked us over. We all sat in terror-stricken silence. I wondered just what evil the guard was preparing to bring down on us. "Well, I've got news for you. Russia is at war!" It seemed to me he took malicious delight in telling us war had been declared three days ago; he knew it all the time but would not tell us. We stared at him in stunned silence. He continued, "Germany declared war on the twenty-second of June and invaded our country and is on its way to Leningrad right now. So, you ungrateful, miserable dogs, maybe now you'll be glad you're here. You've been asking why, why, why, well, now you know. To save your lives, of course!"

I could not believe him. He was having fun at our expense. One man yelled, "It can't be so! Hitler and our leader, Stalin, have an agreement. There can be no war!"

"All right, since you know so much, maybe you'd better talk with Hitler about his agreement. There's the open door. Go on."

There followed great excitement and questions were hurled at the guard faster than he could answer. It seemed everyone talked at once. "That's all I can tell you. Now, shut up all of you." With that he departed; but men continued to shout at each other about the agreement, and mothers cried for their sons and husbands. The older mothers and fathers just shook their heads and started to pray aloud. Yes, these older people prayed. My mother was among them. They had lived through a war and later the revolution. They knew what war meant.

I and my age group just stood around not knowing what to say. Secretly we laughed at them. "Pray, just go ahead and pray, and to whom? There is no God and you know it. We've tried to tell you. What has this so-called God ever done for you? And the priests? What have they done? Good thing they were thrown out."

One of the most terrible things the guard could have done

was to tell us our country was at war while we were cooped up in this prison car—helpless. Never before, or since, have I had such a strong desire to get up and do something violent—anything—just to be active, but here I was and here I would remain who knows how long.

Becoming tired of the praying and pointless arguments, I climbed up to my bunk where I could think for myself. But think about what? The same old questions: Why? Where? To what are we going? But there were no answers.

VIII

Our train continued its way toward the east with more long stops on the spur tracks than ever before. After more than a month of this dreary existence, the train stood all night on a siding. At daybreak the door was unlocked and we saw a guard in his unkempt uniform, hands on hips (a usual pose for those in authority, it seemed), a smirk on his unshaven face, silently surveying us. I stood, scarcely awake, wondering what next. I glanced at Mother but her face showed nothing. Without preamble, the guard took a paper from his pocket and began to read off names. I heard my name called and looked at him.

"Yes, you, Sazonov, and your mother, follow me," he said. "What is this?" I wondered, "a new life or execution?" I climbed out of the car and helped Mother down. We found ourselves in a circle with several others, silent and frightened, all of them.

"You are now on the outskirts of Krasnojarsk," he smiled cryptically, waving his hand in the direction of nowehre in particular. "There are trucks here to take you to the town. You are free to find homes for yourselves and jobs, but you must report to police headquarters every week, without fail, understand? Here are your identification cards."

I was numb with surprise and relief and, at the same time, so consumed with disbelief, I could not step forward to receive our cards. Mother, always the efficient one, prodded me and we stepped forward and signed our names.

Freedom! I could not believe it, but we were so glad to get away from that terrible car it took us only about two minutes to get our things together. It was raining even though it was the middle of summer, but I shouldered our two packs and with a quick nod to our friends we climbed into the truck.

We were let out on what proved to be one of the main streets of the town, a street filled with mud, with a few people foundering around in it.

The first thing to do was to find lodging—an apartment, even a room—and as quickly as possible as the rain was increasing. We walked all day going from door to door. As the day wore on the rain became a downpour until the mud caked on our shoes so thick that walking became very difficult. At every door the answer was the same, "No vacancy." On and on we went to every door on both sides of the streets. The mud became deeper and deeper, even the horses could hardly pull out of it, and it was almost impossible to lift our feet, but we trudged on. I wanted Mother to wait until I searched out a place but she would not hear of it.

"No," she shook her head stubbornly, "we stay together. We'll find something soon. God will take care of His own." I could not understand her great fortitude and this great faith in her God.

She walked on, though I thought each step would be her last. Her heavy coat was soaked from collar to hem and the shawl she had tied on her head looked so heavy with rain that I was afraid she ached all over from holding her head up. The rain streamed down her face, at times blinding her, but still she went on.

Just as it was getting dark, the rain came down as in a cloudburst. I knocked on another door which was opened by a sad-faced woman, and we heard a different answer. "Yes, there's a room you can have." I saw Mother's face light up at the words. "But you'll have to wait for it."

"Why do we have to wait?" I asked impatiently. I felt the irritation building up. "You can see we are very tired and wet. Why wait?" I set down my packs.

The stocky woman with the sad face answered kindly, "There's an old man in the room. He is very sick," she explained, "and expected to die any time. If you want to wait till he dies you can have the room."

"Is there nothing else?" I asked more gently.

"In the meantime you can stay in the empty barn in the rear." She pointed. "There's some straw you can sleep on. I'm sorry that's the best I can offer."

Even this sounded good to us, tired, wet and hungry as we were. As soon as we got into the barn and on that dry straw, I heard Mother offer a prayer of thanks to her God. If she can thank God for this cow barn, I thought, she surely must believe in Him. But as for me, I was more than ever confused. We were both sound asleep under the straw in five minutes. At least we had a roof over our heads.

I went out every day and bought food and reported to police headquarters once a week, as ordered. The rain was insufferable; it did not let up day or night for a whole week. We lived on cold food with the exception of hot tea made with the boiling water given to us by the sorrowful woman in the house.

At the end of two weeks we were informed the old man had died and we could have the room. We spent a whole day cleaning the walls and floors before we could move in. All we had were a clean bed, a black stove freshly scoured, one chair, a rickety table which I scrubbed and scraped with a piece of brick. I bought another bed and chair and a few dishes.

This was a terrible way to begin a new life, but so much better than the cattle car or barn, that we were almost content. At least we could keep clean. But would it last?

IX

Mother soon found work in the textile factory and I could have found a job too, but Mother would not hear of it.

We were sitting at the table after our evening meal and as Mother put her teacup down as a final gesture, she began, "I understand school begins very soon now. Mind you get quite a lot of wood stacked up so it will be easier on you after you start school."

"But, Mother, I don't think I ought to go to the university; we don't know what may happen here in this wilderness. I think I should go to work."

"No, Son, you must go to school. We're lucky to find schools here in this 'wilderness' as you call it. You --- "

"But, Mother --- "

"No argument, please, Son. Your father was an educated man and I know he'd want you to go to school. He's gone now and it's all I can do for him. As long as I can hold a home together, you must go to school."

"But, Mother," I began again, "the situation is different now, we don't know --- "

Mother rose from the table and so did I. She stood with a plate in each hand and looked me squarely in the eye. "Sergei, Son," she emphasized **Son**, "I know best, the same as I knew when your father -- " Suddenly she stopped, turned and went about her dishes. I knew the conversation was ended, so I went out to bring up the next morning's supply of wood and water. But what did she mean, "The same as I knew when your father -- " Always this mystery. I could not help being puzzled over it. As I went down the stairs I remembered once questioning my brother about our father, and his answer, "You've asked me for the last time. Don't ever ask again. And don't ever mention our father's name to anyone else. If you do, I'll beat you very hard—do you hear me? I'll beat you very, very hard." I knew he could do it too, with all his hundred and ninety pounds. But there was no use worrying over it now, so I put it out of my mind.

I enrolled at the university and every afternoon went to the forest to cut wood. Later there was snow, heavy snow, making the work more difficult every day. I built a sled on which to haul the wood, but sometimes the snow was so deep I could scarcely pull it. But the wood kept Mother and me warm and I managed to sell some of it, thus helping to pay my way.

The city of Krasnojarsk is slightly south of Leningrad, and about two thousand miles east. It seemed much colder, as though we were very close to the north pole. The houses were not as well built as the apartment house which had been our home—a stone building with good wood floors and double glass windows. There in Leningrad we enjoyed real comfort compared with this one room in Krasnojarsk.

Mother spent ten hours a day, sometimes more, sitting over a sewing machine, sewing on soldiers' uniforms, always those uniforms for the army. For all her work she received barely enough for our rent and food. We had ration cards but there was never enough food in the markets. It was just like Leningrad, only worse, much worse. Every day I stood in line to buy food; black bread, cabbage, tea, a pound of sugar and sometimes a small piece of pork or sausage.

This life was very hard on Mother. She missed her friends and her own household furnishings she had inherited from her mother, which were old but very good. Here we had only an unpainted board table and miserable beds.

I watched Mother gradually fading in health and spirit. She rose silently now, in the mornings, the early, dark mornings, not confiding in me the way she used to. There was really nothing to talk about; we were locked in a struggle for existence against great odds. There was no time for any cultural activity. The nearby library might just as well not have been there. Mother was too tired to read, even though I brought books home for her. Her long day over the sewing machine and coming home to cook for us was too much for her. When she got home, she wanted only to fall into bed and sleep. I sensed her fear and dread more than ever. Her face had settled into lines and her mouth was a compressed line. This life was mental starvation for her. Our home had become a house of gloom.

As for me, school and a certain amount of friendship and athletic events with boys and girls of my age kept me busy.

X

I had no idea how long we would have to stay in Krasnojarsk. We had been told we were to be here temporarily. Perhaps we would be moved on to some other place, but what did that mean? Could the "other place" be the mines? I remembered how some of our neighbors had disappeared silently overnight, just as we had disappeared, and were never heard of again. I made up my mind we were here as prisoners, and a feeling of permanence seemed to settle down over the whole place. Why? But who was I to question, and of whom could I ask?

With this feeling of permanence growing stronger every day I gave more and more attention to my studies. I read everything I could find and stored more wood for fuel.

One day as I was making my usual weekly report to police headquarters, I was directed to an inner office. I was so frightened at this unusual procedure that I could scarcely breathe, but knew I must make a respectful entrance. My feet were numb as I walked into the next room.

There behind a large desk sat a man—a decent looing chap—in a smart uniform, well-made, and very neatly pressed. I was favorably impressed until he looked up at me with his sharp, piercing, cold blue eyes. All I could think of was ice. He did not speak. He just stared at me, keeping me in suspense. I felt a cold sweat break out all over me. My heart pounded. My tongue seemed to swell in my mouth. I was afraid this man, who probably held my life in his hands, would notice I was shaking as I stood before him, my cap in my hands.

Suddenly he gave me a sardonic smile. A smile of any kind from a high officer in N.K.V.D. service to an underling prisoner like me could mean either of two things: something good for me, or more likely, something bad.

It seemed he kept me waiting for an eternity before he spoke.

"Comrade Sazonov, a grave mistake has been made in the case of Sazonov and mother. You were brought here by mistake and I wish to make amends. I am offering you a period in officers' training school. I have watched you and there is reason to believe you will be a fine officer. What do you say, Comrade?"

There was a strange buzzing in my head and I felt dizzy. My feet, which were numb just a few minutes ago, were hurting and my back began to ache. Here was one of my worst enemies, an officer from N.K.V.D. who had driven us from our home to this wilderness, this prison, speaking to me in a decent tone of voice and calling me "Comrade." Comrade indeed!

Until this moment I was less than a dog, afraid to speak, afraid when spoken to, afraid to be on the street after curfew, and now I'm "Comrade!!"

I think this officer must have noticed my fright, because next he said, "At ease, young man. Report in the morning." With that I relaxed somewhat, but still everything he said sounded unreal. I could not believe he was talking to me.

I burst into our room out of breath and tossed my packages of food on the table. Even in my excitement the regular habit of stopping at the market was obeyed automatically. I knew we must eat.

"Mother, I have great news! I'm to report to officers' training school tomorrow!"

"What's this you say? Officers' training school?" asked Mother as she halted her preparations for our evening meal.

"Yes, they told me today. It's all a mistake that we're here. They took us from home by mistake."

"Now look here, Sergei I'm tired. I had a very heavy day at the factory, and I'm in no mood for jokes."

"It's no joke, Momotchka. It's the truth."

"Well, let me sit down and you tell me quietly what you have to say."

I related word for word what had transpired in the Commandant's office. "Mother, I don't know how I ever got out of there. I almost fell going out the door but when I reached the street my feet weren't heavy. I seemed to have no feet. I don't know how I walked. I seemed to fly. I just somehow got here. I don't know what I bought at the market but I knew we had to have something."

Mother sat staring at me, then without a word she got up and started to examine the packages I brought and began to laugh. "No, you didn't bring what I wanted but it's no worse than it's been many other times. While this is cooking, we can talk."

While I unfolded the tale of how glorious it would be in the army, Stalin's army, I saw Mother's face fall.

"You say he called you 'Comrade'?"

"Yes, Momotchka, 'Comrade'."

"All of a sudden it's a mistake we're brought here like cattle, And all of a sudden you're a fine young man and to become an officer in the army. Has it occurred to you -- "

Then it came back in a rush. The significance of the word **Comrade** hit me with great impact. Suddenly I'm 'Comrade.' I felt sick all over. I could not talk. I could not eat the meal Mother concocted out of the hit and miss groceries I bought in my excitement. Mother tried to talk to me but she suddenly stopped. That same old fear returned and again she was afraid to speak her mind. I knew there was no use insisting. She simply would not talk.

I lay awake most of the night thinking, but no matter what I thought, I knew I must go. I knew the Commandant's gentle "report in the morning," was an order, a military order, that I had to obey.

At breakfast next morning Mother's face was grim and no word was spoken. When I left, Mother kissed me and I saw tears in her eyes.

XI

On reporting to headquarters I was tested, examined, quizzed, measured and fingerprinted until five o'clock and told to come back on the first of the month. This was almost like a reprieve. Two whole weeks!

I ran home as fast as I could and began to make plans. Foremost was my concern for Mother as she was all I had in the world and I was all she had. I was especially concerned because during the long cold winter Mother would be alone. What could I do for her? What could I do? I stood staring at the wood pile in the yard. That was it! Always the diminishing wood pile. Mother must not be cold. Some of the women went out in the forest and cut wood but Mother had never had to do such work, and I did not want her to begin now. This was all I thought of. Mother must be warm mornings and evenings. She was entitled to that—even dumb animals are entitled to "creature comfort"—enough to eat and a warm place to sleep. How could they make us feel so low that we compared ourselves to animals? How could they?

When the time came to leave for training, I had the satisfaction of knowing the room—our home—looked a great deal better than when we moved into it. Mother, always a good housekeeper, scrubbed the place regularly, but the fuel situation continued to worry me. I even dreamed about the deep snow and the bitter cold. Later I found a partial solution. Those of us who lived near enough to the barracks were allowed freedom on Sundays so I spent every Sunday during my many months of training, cutting wood. As soon as my mind was relieved on that score, Mother's loneliness haunted me. None of her old friends were here and she was afraid to make new ones. There was always the fear that spies would report her conversation, so there was no one to share her fireside.

"No, no friends," she repeated sadly. "Always the conversation turns to politics. I have suffered enough on account of too much talk."

"What do you mean, Mother, 'too much talk'?"

We were eating dinner and Mother put her fork down and looked straight at me. "Son, you know from past experience that spies are everywhere. I can't risk any more, so, no friends. I will drink my tea alone, but I wish I had the singing of my samovar to keep me company. How I miss it! Well, the letters you will write me will have to be my companionship."

I did not know what Mother meant when she said, 'I have suffered enough on account of too much talk.' We had always been very careful of our conversation in the home and I never repeated anything outside the family circle. What did she mean? There was always this silence, this fear, this dread.

In the training school there were about one thousand men of different ages. We were arranged in regiments and lived in barracks. The teachers were officers. We studied every day except Sunday. We had a great deal to learn and from the way they hammered it into us I thought new officers must be very much in need. We listened to lectures and demonstrations all day and studied far into the night. With so little time for rest we were always sleepy and often in the classroom during a lecture we nodded in sleep. The punishment for this was to stand for the balance of the lecture, and, if it happened more than once the offender must do night duty around the barracks, which was most difficult after a long day in class. We learned to hold our pencils, during lesson time, in a vertical position on our desks and if our heads fell down they fell on the pencil awakening us with a start. We could only pray the instructor had not noticed. Very often I had a red mark on my forehead showing where I had landed on the pencil.

Sleeping on night sentinel duty meant severe punishment as, I suppose, it is in all countries. The offender was sent to military prison for several days and usually a man guilty of this crime was not allowed to gain officer's rank. The rank of sergeant was as high as he could go. Usually on night duty we ate dry rye bread which was very hard; but if eaten slowly, it helped to fight off sleep.

Our studies included ballistics, topography, artillery, armored defense, anti-tank fight, infantry weapons, weaponry projectory, anti-airplane and general military tactics.

Along with this we had training in the practical use of different kinds of weapons, usually under the worst conditions: very cold weather, deep snow, hard rains, wind and dirt. At the time we had no motor trucks. Everything was horse power and we had to ride every day. I had never been on a horse in my life but, as an officer of artillery, I would be obliged to ride. I had to learn all about horses, their care and feeding, even their cleaning and bedding down.

Political lectures held a very important place in the training. This subject was handled by the Commissar of the school. He showed us in different ways how the Germans were trying to destroy our country, kill most of us, and enslave those they did not kill. He told us of the brutality the Germans were exercising wherever they had gotten into Russia. He read us terrible stories, statements of witnesses, and showed us horrible photographs of atrocities. He also told us about our heroes, who had given their lives for the Fatherland, our Communist party, and Comrade Stalin.

It was no wonder we all burned with desire to die a heroic death with the name of Stalin on our lips. I was one of them. No one was more eager than I to get into the thick of battle as soon as possible. This same eagerness burned in the hearts of two other young men in the class who were with me on that terrible cattle car trip, although we did not mention that trip to anyone.

In the training school we had enough to eat because they wanted us to be strong and have great endurance. However, if there had been more we certainly would have eaten it. The situation in the nearby town was much worse; there was never enough to eat. This was war and the army came first.

During the week I gathered, little by little, different foods from my daily portion, particularly the caloric foods which wouldn't deteriorate: sugar, dried or salted meat or fish, or smoked salami. These things I carefully hid in a secret place where the horse's feed was stored, and on Sunday morning I saw to it that I was first out. I secured my package and took it quickly to Mother. I was never discovered hoarding this food. Each Sunday morning in our home we had a little celebration with the opening of the package, even though Mother was against it. She thought my portion was not enough for me, but I convinced her she was wrong. Since I didn't smoke, I brought her my ration of tobacco which she sold or exchanged for other food. In this way, I managed to keep Mother's health as good as possible.

XII

Our study course was completed in February, 1943. The military ranks were given to us according to one's success in studying: lieutenant, junior lieutenant, or sergeant. Most of us received good grades and were commissioned as lieutenants. I was among them, happy and proud.

Our new officers' uniforms with beautiful shoulder straps looked very good. We elbowed before the only mirror, enjoying our brave appearance and saluting each other without end. The next day we were sworn in as officers of the Red Army. I knew then that we would be shipped out at any moment. However, we were given time to say farewell to our families. I took my horse and got to Mother's door late at night. She was in bed asleep but as soon as she saw me, she knew why I came. "You're going away?" she said and her face whitened as she clutched the door.

"Yes, Momotchka," was all I could answer.

No, she did not cry. She walked around the room as though searching for something while I built up the fire. I could see she did not know just what she was looking for but soon she began to make some tea. For a long time we did not look at each other. We talked about unimportant things, the weather, her work, and how she missed her samovar.

After we drank tea, I said I had to get back soon as the train would leave early in the morning.

"Sergei," began Mother, "I have something to say to you, something I have felt for a long time now that you should know."

I put down my cup and looked at her, wondering. "Yes, Momotchka?"

"You are now going to the front and I may never see you again. This may be my last opportunity to talk with you. I know you are ready to give your life for the Fatherland and for Stalin. For the Fatherland, I say yes; but for Stalin, I say no. For Stalin and his

Communist party, NEVER!"

We sat at the small table, the tea pot and cups between us. Mother resting her arms on the table, never took her eyes off me. With a look of determination on her face, she continued. "Naturally, since the Germans are our enemies, I want you to fight bravely against the enemy of our people; but listen to me carefully. Do you know why we are here in Siberia—in this cold, miserable place —instead of in our apartment where we lived since before you were born? We are not in a concentration camp, it is true, but that is only because of the war and the need for young soldiers and officers. Why do you think they let only those families who had strong men out of the train? Remember the train was side-tracked and officers and doctors came and gave all young men a quick medical examination? The strong ones were chosen to come here. The others were left on the train and we don't know what became of them."

Mother paused and I rose to put more fuel on the fire, as she continued, "Do you know that they freed almost all criminal prisoners from camps in Siberia and made from these men special battalions for the front? They told them then, 'If you will obey orders and fight, your crimes will be forgiven and you'll be free again.' "

"Yes, Mother, I have heard that. It seems to be general knowledge. Also, I've heard they have released nearly all priests because they would preach in the churches against the Germans. Yes, I know the government needs more and more soldiers, but --"

"What do you think would have happened to us, you and me, after we had been dragged from our home if there had been no war? Do you know what kind of future awaited us? We might have been sent to the deep forest, where the snow never leaves, to slave away the rest of our lives. Have you ever thought of that?"

"Yes, Mother, I have thought of that, but I think, and you told me too, that it was a mistake we were put on the train, a mistake, probably -- "

"No, Son, it wasn't a mistake. I have never wanted to talk about this with you until now, but it wasn't a mistake."

"Not a mistake? But what did we do that they deported us to Siberia? I don't understand this, Momotchka."

"I'll tell you all that I tried to shield you from these many years. I have never told you about your father's death. Your father was simply killed, and killed according to Stalin's law. You ask of what he was guilty? I'll tell you. Sometimes in the company of others he remarked about the bad life in our country. He discussed the laws of the regime and thought we should have more liberty, more to eat, and that of better quality. I often told him he talked too much and begged him to be quiet, but I think he felt these things so strongly that he couldn't keep still. One night they knocked on our door. You were sound asleep but Aleksey remembers. They led him away within ten minutes from the time they knocked on the door. No conversation, just, 'Come with us, a little investigation.' He hurriedly dressed, told your brother to take care of the family, and I will never forget the look on his face when he went into the other room and kissed you good-bye, you, our baby son. Officers followed him but at the door he kissed me and squeezed my hand. We didn't see or hear from him for several months. I couldn't find out where he was; there was no trace of him. Then one day they sent for us. We found him in a hospital bed, a white shrunken skeleton of a man. He was dying, and so far gone that he couldn't speak, though I think he recognized us. Aleksey was fifteen and you were eight, but I think you remember."

"Yes, Momotchka, I remember."

"Two days later he died," she said and her face became more grim than usual. "Was he guilty of anything so great that he should be killed?" she continued.

"No."

"And later we were deported to Siberia. Were we guilty of any crime? Am I guilty? And I ask you, have you done anything wrong?"

"No, Mother."

"We are simply what they call 'social enemies.' That is what your father was. He was not a member of the Communist party. He didn't like Stalin's rule and said so, and for that reason they killed him and later deported us to Siberia. Our home is gone and everything we held dear. All our possessions are gone. We don't know where Aleksey is and he doesn't know where we are. Nothing is left but memories of your father and your brother."

Mother almost lost her self control and was silent for a few minutes sitting quietly at the table. Then she continued, "Can you now say, 'Fatherland and Stalin' in the same breath? Or can you honestly believe it was a mistake that they brought us here? And those hundreds of people who were on the train with us and the millions more in the camps, are they also mistakes? You saw and talked with them. Were they any different from us?"

I nodded my head in agreement.

"Son, you are an officer now and will go to the front to fight for our people. I hope you won't forget your father. You know the truth about him now and know that he was a good man. He loved us all. I understand that it is very hard for you to listen to all of this, but I had to tell you. I know you will think it over and the time will come when you will say, 'Mother was right.' Maybe we will never see each other again. Be careful. I know you will do your duty well, but I don't want you to perish for Stalin and the Communist party or for those who killed your father and sent us here. Don't forget God, the God I know you believe in, in spite of your teachings. I say again, don't forget God and He will always be with you."

With these words Mother put her head on the table and sobbed bitterly. It was nearly dawn and I had a long way to go, so I kissed her and whispered, "Momotchka" and stole out of the room.

The snow had stopped and the thermometer was dropping; I could feel it getting colder by the minute. All was white and quiet. Here and there I could see a faint light in a window; otherwise, the only light came from the moon as it shone on the icicles hanging from the eaves of houses. Not a soul was out. The only sound was the crunching of my horse's hooves in the frozen crust of snow. It seemed to me this was the coldest, quietest and most lonely night I had ever seen. Well, if I was lonely, mother must be even lonelier, sitting as she was in that miserable room she was forced to call home. She was alone with her thoughts of her family. All of us were gone now. "Dear Momotchka," I thought, "God keep you. 'God?' What am I saying? Well, yes, God keep you, Momotchka."

The last time I saw her was at the railroad station the next day. There she stood in her shabby black coat, with a shawl tied over her head. My Momotchka, wearing one of those ugly shawls, just like a peasant, Mother, who had always worn a hat. How I hated to see her in this peasant garb, but the day was cold and the snow was deep and it was a miracle she could get there at all. How many, many long blocks she had walked in the freezing cold just to see me once more. Her face was gray. It seemed the pallor of death was on her face, but her shoulders were square and she held her head high. No one in the world could see how she suffered, but I knew. She did not cry, but said over and over, "I'll never see you again, never, never." I couldn't answer for fear of breaking down, but as I climbed the high steps of the Russian train, I lifted my hand in silent salute to my mother.

XIII

The troop train was exactly like the one in which I had been imprisoned on the way to Siberia nearly two years before—a long line of cattle cars with boards built into shelves for beds. The difference was there were not so many of us, and these travelers were a noisy, happy crowd.

We were all new officers mostly about twenty years old, and we were now out on our own for the first time. To be an officer meant a great deal to us. We felt the world was ours to do with as we wished. Maybe we would be dead in a short time, but that was not important. We had just received our first pay as officers so with money in our pockets, drinking was the order of the day. Drinking, dancing and singing. The more we drank the more we danced and when we couldn't stay on our feet any longer we sat down—"sprawled" is a better word—and sang. There were duets and quartets but mostly ensemble. We sang everything we knew, but one song in particular, a famous Russian song about our homeland, was repeated over and over again until it became a drunken garbled mixture:

"My homeland is broad and great -
There are many forests, fields and rivers,
I don't know of any other state
Where people breathe so freely -
Free, that's it, that's us, free—whoopee—free"

And from way down at the end of the car, a big officer with a fine bass voice waved a bottle in the air and took up the next line:

"And no one in the world
Can laugh and love as well as we."

With that everyone joined in, singing together, or trying to, and falling all over each other until, in a drunken stupor, we fell asleep.

As for the dancing, I have never seen better, and I have never witnessed better or harder drinking. At every station where we stopped the peasants greeted us with samogon, * gallons and gallons of it. They made it from potatoes and there was always plenty, and the peasants were glad to have the money we paid them, though they did not overcharge. We, the soldiers, were heroes. We were on the way to war to save the homeland, and nothing was too good for us.

No one in my group seemed to have a care in the world; no one was afraid of the front, of death. We were young and we did not value our lives. Nothing mattered. We were drunk and free to do as we liked. I was as bad as any of them and drank with the best of them. But when I began to sober up, everything was different. I saw life from another point of view. My present situation, my responsibility to Mother, good, kind Momotchka, was ever uppermost in my mind. It seemed only a few minutes ago that we sat in our home talking about Communism, Stalin, my Godless world. I sat thinking of Mother and her loving belief in God and her faith and hope that I would believe the same. She said she knew I would, in spite of what I had learned in school and tried to teach her. Dear Momotchka, God keep you, God—what am I saying? There it was again, 'God'—I, praying to God to keep Mother!

A hand suddenly clapped me on the back. "What! You're going thoughtful on us again? Aw, come on! Drink and make up for all that time we lost in training. Remember? Come on! Here's a bottle." So I drank more and more vodka until the first day and night on the way to the front was one great big celebration.

The next sober period was worse than the first. We were getting farther and farther away from home, even from the barracks, and my real home, Leningrad. Would I ever see Leningrad again?

My mind traveled back to my childhood. I remembered the day it was announced that all children who could not pay, could not go to school any longer, and a week later the names of those who had not paid were read off and told to leave. When Boris' name was read, my world seemed to drop. He had been my friend and playmate since the first grade, and now in the eighth grade he must

---

*Vodka

leave school. I felt I would never see him again. As he rose from his seat to leave, he turned to look at me, and then his eyes turned to the wall in front of the room where, "You must study and study and study," was written in large letters. This was signed by Lenin. I knew what Boris was thinking.

Then I remembered the scene of the icons and holy pictures being taken down from the walls and Mother saying, "It is better this way." These things and many others flooded my memory: the terrible train trip with its disgraceful way of living in such closeness to which Mother and I were not accustomed. And last, Mother's talk with me the night before I left. Oh, miserable me! Who am I? Where am I? What am I? Pour me another drink, somebody. I am an officer in the army and I must go to the front and fight the enemy to save my people and my Russia! And I will fight!

I really wanted to fight the enemy for the liberty of Russia, and, as it had been drummed into me so consistently that we were fighting for our "beloved leader, Stalin," I was anxious to fight for him. He had been held up to me all through my school days and especially in officers' training as a perfect man, a model, the savior of our country, and the freedom of our people. He really took the place of God in my heart. I would have given my life for him.

But as I sat there in the noisy, uncomfortable train over and over the same thoughts raced through my mind. At last the mystery of my father was clear, but what to do? What to think? I had to agree Mother was right. Father was a good man and all he wanted was freedom from want and worry. Well, that's what I wanted too, and here I was going out to fight for it. I gave up.

XIV

I arrived at my headquarters in February, 1943. After a very short interview I was nominated for the duty of the Commander of a Reconnaissance Unit and was directed to an artillery regiment, stationed at the front somewhere near Kursk. My main job was to establish a reconnaissance post from where my men and I could observe the enemy's lines continually. When necessary, I had to direct the fire of our four 76mm cannons, which were hidden a few miles behind my watching post. Our only connection with the cannon unit was the telephone line; the radios were received much later.

My first days at the front were something I will never forget. Even though I was nineteen years old and had some experience with death, I had never come face to face with violent death. I arrived at my unit just after our attack; the Germans retreated so fast that they didn't have time even to bury their dead. Bloody, distorted, and bare-footed bodies were lying in the dirty snow on both sides of the road. We passed by, leaving them where they were for our work troops to bury. That was their job. Ours was to kill.

Always before me were the lessons which had been drummed into us in the classes and more recently, the newspapers which were made up especially for soldiers at the front. We must fight to protect our beloved country from Hitler's Germany and the rest of the world, too, if they should happen to decide to march on us. We believed all we were told: "We are the largest and best country in the world." Some of us had heard that Europe and the USA were much better off than Russia, but that was attributed to Capitalistic propaganda. We were told the laborers there were all held in slavery to the Capitalists and no hardship was too much to endure for the sake of our Russian freedom.

In July, 1943 the Germans began a sudden attack near Kursk, where, just a few months ago, a big quantity of war prisoners were captured by our troops. One day I happened to be near the camp where the captured Germans were quartered just in time to see them being evacuated. I was surprised to see that there were only four or five thousand Germans, not the 150,000 which I knew had been taken. The prisoners were tottering and stumbling along the road, completely enervated. There were also several Russian peasant wagons pulled by worn out horses. In these wagons, sitting and lying one on top of the other, were Germans, who, it seemed, couldn't walk. Russian soldiers walked beside this terrible column and I asked one of them, "What is this? Where are the rest of them? We captured about 150,000 men."

"It is true," he answered, then added indifferently, "Typhus," and went on.

I stood there and watched two Germans who were trying to catch a wagon. Apparently they just could not walk any further and wished only to hold on to the wagon for support. A Russian soldier yelled at them and raised his gun. One of them, frightened, gathering his last strength, turned back and joined the walking column but the second man held stubbornly and desperately to the wagon. I heard a shot and the man fell down. Someone yelled, "You deserve this. 'As you make your bed, so must you lie on it.'" The column went on, the men stepping over the dead body in the road. Terrible picture! Why did I happen to be here to see it? I tried to justify to myself this treatment of prisoners, but I could not. It was such a cruel and inhuman act.

XV

In October, 1943 our units had just captured a small town near Poltava in Ukrainia, though it wasn't exactly a town. It was only what remained of it, after a heavy battle. The enemy had been forced to leave and all was in ruins. We came through this burned-out town at night and finally found a road. A heavy snow was falling and we made very slow progress.

Suddenly ahead of us we noticed movement and, thinking it might be a straggler of the German army, I called, "Halt! Who goes there?"

In answer we heard a child's voice speaking in a language none of us could understand. I advanced and found two children, a boy about twelve and a little girl about eight, pulling a large sled. They were dressed in adult coats and big shoes. They looked very funny, though none of us laughed.

I dismounted and walked over to them. After listening closely to half Russian and half Ukrainian, I tried to talk to them. "Where are you children going in the middle of the night in this deep snow?"

"We are going to our uncle. He lives in the next village."

"Why are you pulling this heavy sled?"

"This is our mother," answered the little girl. "She is very tired and is sleeping now."

I looked at the sled and was about to speak when the boy came up to me. I leaned down to him and he said very low, almost in a whisper, "She is dead, not sleeping. She--" indicating his sister, "thinks our mother is asleep. Don't tell her. She is too little to understand things like this."

I looked at his pale thin face and into his eyes which looked as if they had seen thousands of deaths in this time of war, but I didn't know what to say to him. What words are there to comfort a child in the midst of his greatest tragedy?

We took the shivering children on the horses and one of our men drew the sled and we started on to the next village, the boy directing us. When we got there, as usual, there were no houses. All was in ruins. We could smell from a distance the unpleasant odor of burning, the odor that was our faithful companion during the war in Ukrainia. The Germans, as they ran, set fire to everything, trying to stop our advance at any cost.

When the hospital wagon caught up with us, we put the children in it where they could have care and food. "Where is my mother? I want my mother!" cried the little girl.

The children were with us a couple of days, until we found a village where they were cared for. The Germans, in their haste, had not taken time to burn this village, knowing we Russians were just behind them.

During the fighting in the Ukraine territory I tried to keep up a correspondence with Mother, although it was very difficult due to our continuous moving so I heard from her very seldom. At best, our letters were brief because we were told the army had great difficulty handling all the mail; and, of course, every letter was censored. I waited impatiently for each letter from Mother, hoping she might have news of my brother. Leningrad had been blockaded and while I was in officers' training we heard over the radio that our troops had driven the Germans out and ended the siege. When correspondence became possible again, I learned what had taken place.

The siege began a few days after we left on our terrible trip to Ukrainia and before it ended, a million and a half Russians had died of hunger and disease. Soldiers received a bowl of soup and about a pound of bread daily; civilians, a quarter of a pound of bread. The Germans bombarded the city with artillery as well as aircraft. The water system was destroyed and the only water to be had came from a lake. I remembered Mother saying to me before I left for the front, "You see, Son, it is the wish of God that we are here in Siberia. The ways of God are unfathomable."

My officer's salary was transferred to my Mother regularly every month. Almost every one of my fellow officers did the same for their families. It was a big relief for me to know that my mother, at least, would not be hungry or without firewood.

Of course, my life at that time was occupied with the usual things of war; but when there was a slight lull between attacks and bombardments, I would begin to think again about everything that had happened in my life. Always thinking. I couldn't stop it. There was no vodka to ease the tension. It was only before an attack that the men were issued a cup of vodka. Vodka for everyone! Vodka for courage! Sometimes it was two cups and then I saw the half drunken infantry run with a "hurrah" directly into the enemy's machine guns. They fell en masse, but were followed by more and more men. They simply trampled down the Germans. Of course, our command didn't need to spare the lives of these men. There were so many men that life was cheap.

A few months after arriving at the front, I knew our losses were about five million. We were told German losses were half of their army, but we were not told how many that was. I heard later the German army had two million men. Most of them were Germans. The rest was made up of Satellite forces (Hungary and others), but I never knew for certain how many men the Germans had.

XVI

As our units crossed Ukrainia at Kremenchug, we lost contact with the enemy. Due to the fatigue of our men, we stopped in a half-ruined town and gave the troops twelve hours rest. After a little sleep I took a walk around the town. It was late evening and all was quiet as I went from one street to another. Suddenly I heard some strange cries emanating from a building. I hurried there and found it was a German hospital filled with wounded Germans who had been left behind in the hasty retreat.

I decided to investigate all of the rooms. I opened one door and entered a very large room dimly lit by a kerosene lamp. The scene was terrible. The room was filled with wounded German soldiers lying on their beds. Some were bandaged with bloody bandages, moaning and crying. Others were lying on the floor as there were not enough beds. Several of them lay motionless, apparently dead or unconscious. The stench was nauseating.

But most awful and ugly was the scene in a corner of the room where lay three wounded German nurses. Two of them were fighting desperately with two of our soldiers who were trying to rape them. The nurses, it seemed, were wounded in their arms or legs. Our soldiers, obviously drunk, were pulling the blankets away from the girls, laughing wildly. I hurried over there, grabbed them and shoved them away. "You dirty animals! You damned monsters!" I yelled at them.

They looked at me, saying, "What are you yelling about? They are Germans, damned fascists! And what did they do to our wives and daughters?"

"But these women are wounded, you idiots!"

"Wounded? I don't see that they have lost anything that we would need," one of them yelled, and they both howled with stupid laughter.

I couldn't take any more of this and struck the nearest one in the face. As he fell to the floor, I turned to the other one and found myself looking into a machine gun. "What's this?" I asked calmly, realizing too late they were much drunker than I had thought. They were absolutely crazy.

"Hand it over at once!" I ordered, but the other soldier was beside him with another machine gun aimed at me.

"Now you listen to us, you greenhorn! Nobody will stop us, understand? Don't touch it, Lieutenant!" he yelled as he noticed my hand reaching for my pistol. I knew they would kill me without regard for the consequences if I cried out for help. At that moment I felt the presence of one of them behind me. I dodged to the left and in the same movement pulled down a table with a lamp on it. At the top of my voice I yelled, "Fire! Fire!" I saw them in a daze look at the fire, which was barely starting; and, making use of their confusion, ordered, "You, run for help quick, and you, help me take these people out of here!" If they had not been so stupidly drunk—or so well trained to take orders—my ruse never would have worked.

"Yes, Tovarish Lieutenant!" they answered automatically, forgetting the German nurses.

With the help of other soldiers who were attracted to the scene, we carried the Germans out. Since there was no water and no chance to extinguish the fire, we had to take everyone out. Some were dead, but there was no time to find out who were dead and who were alive. Several of our soldiers suffered minor burns; two of them were injured seriously.

I didn't report these two drunken soldiers, though I wanted to many times whenever I recalled the terrible scene. Several months later these two men were killed in an attack.

XVII

As time passed, relations with my soldiers became very good; I was trying to be not only their superior but their friend as well. There were times when some of them told me about their past life, but such a friendly gesture might very well be usual in times of war.

One of them, a peasant from Siberia about thirty years old, became very talkative one evening as we sat in our trench:

"My father was a Kulak* but before the revolution we were very poor peasants. After the revolution we were given some land, the same as other peasants. My brother fought in the Red Army and lost his life. I was just a little fellow but I remember the day when my mother and father received the word he was dead."

He stopped talking, and seemed to be thinking of his home and that terrible day. I said nothing to encourage him to talk, but soon he began again.

"Our whole family worked very hard on our land and we prospered, but in 1930 the government charged us such high income taxes that we couldn't pay it. Then Bolsheviks came to our village and took everything we had. House, land, cows, horses—all, all. That's another day I'll never forget. The cows and horses. Especially the horses, when I saw them led away. I loved our horses. Oh, it was awful," and the poor man could scarcely hold back the tears.

"We, together with other kulaks in the neighborhood with their whole families, were loaded into railroad freight cars." Yes, I knew all about the freight cars! He continued, "We were so closely packed together we had to stand. No one could sit down. The suffering was terrible and in that condition we were sent to camps

---

*Well-to-do farmer

in Siberia.

"My mother and father and I were put to work in a mine, but the work was so heavy we couldn't do it. Then they gave us nothing to eat. Yes, if you couldn't work, you couldn't eat. My parents died, starved to death. I stayed out of sight as much as I could. One day as I was hiding in a forest a Mongol, who was hunting there, found me and took me to his home."

Suddenly he stopped talking and stared at me. "My God, Lieutenant, what have I been saying? I shouldn't have told all this. I've talked too much. I beg you, Lieutenant, not to repeat what I've said. I could get into terrible trouble for this! I beg you!"

"Never mind, my friend, your story is safe with me. I'll forget you said a word. So now rest easy."

Great God! I thought after listening to this awful story. This is the fate that would have awaited my mother and me if I hadn't been picked for officers' training. Probably we would have starved to death! I learned that about one million Kulak families were deported to Siberia. Who knows how many of them survived?

Another soldier told me about a huge territory by the Ural Mountains somewhere near the city of Kirov, not far from the River Kama. This place was called "Prohibition Zone." In this camp lived hundreds of thousands of prisoners. He also told me of a settlement near the Volga which was made up of Germans from the Autonomous Province. These prisoners had been deported wholesale from their lands immediately after the beginning of the war on the charge of **betraying Soviet Russia.** Among these Germans were different criminal and political prisoners and a large group of Japanese from the Far East charged with espionage.

A soldier from Kuban Cossack Territory told me the Cossack population was deported to Siberia from their fatherland in 1932 because they refused to join the collective farms. Another soldier told me about a camp near Solovetsk where a great number of priests were imprisoned.

These men were afraid to talk about themselves. Sometimes in the loneliness of the night their memories would pour from them like tears. Perhaps they never realized they were verbalizing their thoughts.

After looking at these men and listening to them, certain parts of Stalin's Constitution, which I had memorized, flooded back into my mind: Article 123: "Any direct or indirect restriction of the rights of citizens on account of their race or nationality are punishable by law." Article 124: "Freedom of religious worship is recognized for all citizens." Article 125: "The citizens of U.S.S.R. are guaranteed by law: A) freedom of speech; B) freedom of the press; C) freedom of the assembly; D) freedom of street processions and demonstrations." Those were the promises we had been given, but they were all contrary to fact. Words—just meaningless words.

One day I read in our newspaper that the Germans had discovered, near Smolensk, a mass grave of the twelve thousand Polish officers who were killed by the Russians in 1940, during the time of the Russian occupation. Russia claimed the story was German propaganda and that actually these Polish officers were massacred by the Germans in 1941 when the Russian army withdrew from Smolensk. I knew the Germans had committed brutalities, so of course I believed the Germans did it. But after all that had happened to my family and what I saw and heard in Siberia and here in the army, who knew? The Russians had the same reasons for killing Polish officers as Germany had. And I wondered if the Russian N.K.V.D. were not as cruel as the German Gestapo.

Life in the army and this war taught me to think.

XVIII

Early in the spring of 1944 our troops had just burst the German defense fortifications after intense artillery fire. The enemy abandoned their positions and fled. The rain and mud did not stop them; they just ran. Our infantry and tanks advanced carefully after crossing the enemy's abandoned trenches. We, the artillery, followed about a mile behind them.

Four of us advanced on foot—my Captain, two men and I. Suddenly the Captain decided to look into an empty trench that was built like an underground room and was covered with tree trunks and dirt. He went in and the next moment I was horrified to hear him yelling at the top of his voice, "Germans! Germans!"

We heard several shots; then all was quiet. By this time I knew the trench was not empty. Inside were Germans and I was certain my Captain was dead. The two men with me grabbed hand grenades intending to throw them into the trench, but I stopped them on the slim chance the Captain might still be alive. As I was about to rush into the trench the men stopped me, yelling, "You'll be killed too!"

I ordered the men to throw grenades on the cover of the trench and a moment later I rushed in with my pistol in my hand. Inside it was dark, with the dust and dirt falling from the ceiling where the grenades had exploded. One of the Germans shot at me, but the bullet went wild because I had knocked his gun with my left hand and jammed my pistol into his face. He dropped the gun to the ground and put up his hands. Two other Germans were strangling my Captain on the ground. One of them was holding his hand over the Captain's mouth so he couldn't make a sound.

I kicked one of them with my heavy boot and yelled, "Hands hoch! Alle raus!"* All three raised their hands and marched out

*Hands up! Everybody out!

where my men grabbed them.

I hurried over to the Captain and found he had a bullet through his chest. We delivered him to the proper attendants and later heard he was recovering. He wrote to me from the hospital thanking me for saving his life.

During the Captain's absence, it was expected that I would be promoted, temporarily at least, to the Captain's position since I was the ranking officer. But such was not the case. The position was given to the junior Lieutenant. He was a Communist. This was a very embarrassing situation, but I had to make the best of it. There was no doubt that they knew I came from a family of non-communists as headquarters had the complete history of every man and his family. They probably knew all about my father long before I did.

Shortly after the affair where the Captain was nearly killed, we took over a small town in Rumania, which had been completely abandoned by its inhabitants. The peoplc couldn't have been gone more than a couple of days as everything looked fresh, even though there were signs of a hurried departure. Naturally we searched these houses very cautiously, looking for Germans who might have been left behind. We found no one, but what we did find gave us much comfort. The first house we entered, gun in hand, was a comfortable little house of about five rooms and a bathroom. Several of the men with me were from Siberia and had never seen a bathroom. One of them stood looking at the tub, wondering what that long box-like looking thing could be. I watched him as he ran his fingers along its smooth surface, an expression of bewilderment on his face. Someone yelled, "I'll bet it's a bath tub. I heard of one once."

After his surprise was over, we laughed and proceeded to heat water and everybody took a quick bath. What a wonderful treat it was! All our bathing in Leningrad and Siberia was done in public showers.

But our first introduction to the European way of life was interrupted suddenly by the order from our headquarters, "Take your positions immediately. Prepare for the attack."

XIX

The attack was to begin exactly at eight o'clock in the morning. At seven we, the artillery, were to open fire on the enemy's fortifications and continue until eight when the infantry would go to the attack. I, with several soldiers, was in the reconnoitering point, in order to direct the artillery fire.

A few minutes before seven I stood looking at the enemy's lines with my binoculars, waiting to start firing.

"Tovarich Lieutenant! A call for you from headquarters!" I took the telephone.

"Yes?"

"Lieutenant Sazonov, an officer of the infantry will come to you at once, a Lieutenant Morozov. Please cooperate during the attack. Understand?"

"Yes, Tovarich Colonel!" Returning to my place, not thinking too much about the phone call—it was a usual thing—I continued my watching. A few minutes later I heard my name called and turned to see an officer looking at me.

"I am Lieutenant Morozov!"

"Welcome," I answered and saluted mechanically. Then as I looked at him more closely, I knew. This face—I have seen it before—yes, I know this man. Who was he and where had I met him? In the next moment I noticed the raspberry color of his military emblems and recognized him. Yes, no doubt of it. He was one of the men who had come into our house in Leningrad in June of 1941. He was the sergeant who had struck my mother that terrible night. That scene flashed once again before my eyes. I saw my mother fall to the floor near the wall. I saw the blood on her face. As the brutal scene hit my mind, I forgot everything—the attack, the plan of battle, everything. I wanted only to hit him—to see blood on his face, his cruel face. I lunged forward. He looked at me, his face filled with amazement as he no doubt saw the rage in my face. In that second three red rockets lighted the sky behind his head.

"Signal to fire!" he yelled.

"Fire!" I cried to my telephone man.

"Fire!" he shouted into the phone, and the artillery opened fire on the enemy.

This sudden movement into battle interrupted my impulse to smash him. I managed to control myself. Lieutenant Morozov probably thought my emotion was due to the firing signal and in this exciting moment had no time to think more about it. We stood side by side watching the enemy lines through binoculars. I directed the firing.

I was sure that Morozov didn't recognize me. My strange behavior a few minutes before hadn't excited any special interest. I was only one small case in thousands in his rich practice of routing people out of their homes before the war. Who could know how many cases had passed through his hands? He was a Lieutenant now, and he had no doubt earned this title with "hard" work in his loathsome profession. Thank God, I had succeeded in controlling myself. To strike a Secret Police Officer—I put it out of my mind.

We stood there commenting about our firing. I tried not to look at that hated face, fearing a new eruption of venom.

Suddenly he said with a smile, "Look over there. Those are my brave soldiers. Soon they will go to the attack."

I took my binoculars. "But, Lieutenant, I don't understand. I see movements in the infantry's trenches, soldiers moving to the right and some to the left of where they are to attack!"

"Just keep looking and you'll get wise. You must be new here? Recently from school? Well, I'll explain to you how it works. See those soldiers filling in the empty space?"

"Yes, I see, but look, they have no weapons! The soldiers moving to the left and right are armed, but these men ... "

"So! Well, for your information, those are my brave boys, the Penalty Battalion," he answered with seeming pride.

The penalty battalion! I heard about these ill-fated battalions many times, but I never saw them in action. But no weapons—What ... ? I wondered.

"You just watch. They'll be given weapons just before they attack. You don't think we could supply them with guns while we hold them as prisoners in the rear, do you?"

I looked at him in amazement. Yes, he was just the right man for the job.

"You know," he continued, "the penalty battalion can't be

trusted, made up as it is of soldiers and officers who have broken the military discipline. They're getting now only what they deserve. They have to take the brunt of the attack. When they get out in front there, if they turn back, our military police will fire on them to keep them going."

I listened horrified.

"You should know officers who have been sentenced to the penalty battalion are degraded to privates for a period of time, one to three months, maybe more."

"And when they come back?"

"**If** they come back, you mean," Morozov answered with a wicked grin on his face. "This punishment means almost certain death; but if anyone lives through it, he may be reinstated to his former rank."

He must have seen the horror on my face as he hastened to add, "You must understand, Lieutenant, this is a necessary measure to maintain strong discipline in our army. Besides, it gets rid of a lot of no-goods. True, it takes a lot of military police to guard these fellows, but most of all it gives the Command enough men for the initial attack," he finished, satisfied with this reasonable explanation.

I looked at my watch. It was a few minutes before eight and the guards began to pass out the hand bombs and hand machine guns to the penalty battalion. Exactly at eight o'clock the artillery stopped firing and the soldiers of the penalty battalion jumped from the trenches and rushed toward the enemy's lines. At first it seemed to me they would capture the enemy easily and without sacrifice, but I was wrong. When they got close to the German lines two heavy machine guns opened with devastating fire on our men. It was horrible to see, as dozens of them fell dead or wounded. I looked at Morozov's face. He was watching this scene with a look of pure enjoyment. It made me think of how the Romans must have enjoyed watching the gladiator fights. Then I noticed some of the men were trying to run or crawl back to our trenches. The face of Morozov began to twist. He grabbed the telephone connected with his battalion and ordered, "Return those dogs to their places at once!"

I looked out. There were the soldiers who were trying to return to our trenches, but now, after Morozov's order, his guards opened machine gun fire on them, his own men. (Caesar turned his thumb down.) Several men fell. The rest of them tried to find salvation in the holes of bomb shells.

Morozov turned to me. "Lieutenant Sazonov, order your artillery to fire on those machine gun nests. Now you know their exact positions."

"But Lieutenant, your men are too close, we will kill our own men!"

"It is not for you to decide, Lieutenant," he answered in a harsh voice, "and do as I tell you, immediately!"

I stood there looking at him, wondering how I could stop him.

"Haraho,* Morozov. Permit your people to return to our trenches and I will destroy those machine guns at that moment," I answered, trying desperately to think of something to do.

"This is a foolish loss of time! Do you know that these people, as you call them, will die sooner or later? They are the penalty battalion, understand? They rate death anyway, but were given the opportunity to die in glory and for a profit of our Fatherland!" He stopped to catch his breath and then continued in his steel-like voice, threateningly, "Okay, will you do this right away or shall I report you to your Colonel?"

I had no choice. "Prepare to fire," I called to the telephone man and began to give exact coordinations of the enemy's machine guns, at the same time keeping an eye on Morozov. He took his binoculars and began to watch his battalion.

All right, here is my chance, I thought. I hurriedly clipped the telephone wire which lay at my feet, and placed my heavy boots over the cut ends while I continued to give the firing instructions.

Suddenly the telephone man shouted, "Tovarich Lieutenant, the phone connection is broken!" Morozov began to swear with rage and went to the phone.

In a strict voice, I gave the orders, "Everybody, quick, check the wires outside. Hurry! Hurry! Don't stand there—you heard me! Move!"

The men ran out, while Morozov sat at the phone yelling, "Allo!**Allo!" I stood there pretending to study the maps and trying to hide my smile. Morozov couldn't see me from where he sat, so, unseen I prepared a piece of tape with which to put the cut ends of the wire together, later.

I took the binoculars again. Down there the groups of des-

---

* All right

**Hello

perate men, seeing no other choice, were still trying to go stealthily closer to the enemy's machine guns. They slunk closer and closer and then, at exactly the same time, they started to run toward the machine guns from different directions. Some fell down, but a few threw their hand bombs. To my great surprise, they made it. There were several explosions and the enemy machine guns were silent. Our regular infantry rushed from the trenches and ran forward, but there was no more enemy fire. In a second I put the telephone wire together and a moment later Morozov started to yell, "Lieutenant, Lieutenant, the phone is connected. Quick, order the fire."

I was silent.

"Do you hear me, Lieutenant?" He was there beside me.

"You don't need it now," I answered. "Just take a look out there."

He grabbed his binoculars and saw that the Germans had been pushed back. The remainder of his soldiers were coming back slowly. Morozov looked at me and I could see he was angry that things hadn't gone as he wanted. He seemed to be trying to tell me something. At last he said, with a forced smile, "Good, very good." He saluted me and added sarcastically, "Thanks for the cooperation." Then he turned and strode away.

I watched him as he disappeared and thought, "You are lucky, Lieutenant Sergei Sazonov, that you managed to control yourself. If you had struck him it would have meant your death. You found a little satisfaction in defeating him; it isn't much. However, the main thing was the lives of those men, but you did get the best of an N.K.V.D. lieutenant; a great thing. It will be better if you can be lucky enough never to meet him again."

But who knows? "Gora s goroj ne sostojetsja, a chelovek s chelovékom sastanetsja!"*

---

*The mountains cannot meet each other, but people will meet." (A Russian proverb)

XX

Somewhere in Rumania my Captain, recovered, returned to the regiment. He was surprised when he found the junior lieutenant instead of me in his place, but he said nothing. He occupied his old position again and we became very good friends. He had been in the war from almost the very beginning and was a highly intelligent man. He was a Communist, but he never tried to enter into political conversations. We simply avoided such dangerous topics. He was very reserved. Everyone liked him because of his genuineness and endurance. Only once did I see him when it seemed he could not withstand things as they were. We were sitting in our trench and he was reading a book. All at once he threw the book down in a rage and strode out uttering an oath, but all I heard was: "I would just like to see how it will be later."

I picked up the book, "Order of the Day," by Stalin, and looked at what he had been reading—"a great and historic occasion for our army," ... "we are fighting not for conquest but for a nobler aim," ... "our army was not created for the purpose of conquest of foreign countries." There was also a short statement by A. Gorkin, Secretary of the presedium of the Supreme Soviet of the U.S.S.R.: "We have not and cannot have any such war aims as that of imposing our will and our regime upon the Slavic or other enslaved nations of Europe who are expecting our help. Our aim is to help these nations in their struggle for liberation from Hitler's tryanny and then leave them to organize their lives and their own lands as they see fit."

On June 6, 1944 we had a big celebration in my regiment. It had been announced over the radio that American and British troops landed at Normandie and opened a second front against Germany. Now we were sure Germany would be defeated. We officers received new uniforms which were made in Russian factories from American and British materials. Stalin wanted his troops, the officers especially, to be well dressed when they entered European countries. Our old uniforms looked very much the worse for wear.

In August, 1944, the enemy succeeded in regrouping their forces at new defensive positions, after a long retreat. Our troops had to stop and prepare for a new attack. We dug our trenches opposite the German lines and began to exchange artillery fire. Several days passed, then one day enemy shell-fire cut our telephone wire which connected us with the infantry staff. It was still daylight, so we couldn't send a man to fix it right away; it was in the open space and the Germans could spot him too easily.

We waited for darkness, hoping the enemy wouldn't throw out light rockets too often. Our telephone men would repair the line without trouble; it was a routine job to them, simply fasten two wires together and tape them. The man was to crawl along the wire until he reached the first end, then find the other end which should be very near. We knew the possible place of the break; it was best to go there from the infantry's trenches in front of and below us. Our trenches were on top of a hill.

The man went out to fix the line; and we, my Captain and I, thought everything would be all right, as by that time the enemy was not throwing light flares very often. However, about a half hour later we heard intense machine gun fire and saw many light rockets around the place where we thought the break would be found. We felt that something was wrong, but we couldn't see anything from our trench because there was a bend in the hill. Expecting the worst, we sent a soldier to find out what had happened to the telephone man. In a short time he returned and said the man was dead. The Germans had brightened the night more than ever. The Captain called our staff at once but the answer was, "Try once more."

This time I decided to go with the man to the infantry's trenches, since this was the shortest distance to the broken telephone line. The Germans were throwing their flares very rapidly. It was a bad spot to send anyone. The only way to do this job was to rush out just after one light died down, run a few seconds, then lie down before another rocket would light up the ground. This process must be repeated again and again until the broken line was found.

I looked at the man. He was an old, experienced soldier, who knew his job very well. I couldn't see any trace of fear on his bony, gaunt face. Surely, he was accustomed to the everyday dangers during the long years of the war, but still, this task was a very dangerous one.

"Don't take too much of a risk," I said to him. "If you see you can't make it, come back at once."

He nodded, then quietly, "Harasho, Comrade Lieutenant."

He then crawled carefully out of the trench and lying down, waited for the time to run. He started, and got about fifty feet away when a rocket lighted the sky above him. He hit the ground but it was too late. The Germans saw him and opened fire. The bullets raised dust all around him as he lay on the ground; the rockets lighting unceasingly. Suddenly he rose and began to run back, but after a few steps he fell. It all happened within a very few seconds and without a thought I rushed out of the trench, grabbed him and dragged him to the trench into which we simply tumbled. The man moaned; he was badly wounded in the leg. I couldn't believe that I wasn't hit and only then I realized what I had done. If I had taken time to think, I probably couldn't have done it.

The soldier was carried off by the attendants and I returned to my own trench. When the Captain heard all that had taken place he said, "I'll report to the staff and tell them we'll put down a new phone line in another direction. We'll find a way where it's less dangerous and have it ready in the morning."

I saluted him and went to my corner to sleep. I had barely closed my eyes when I heard the Captain's voice.

"Bad news, Lieutenant."

I couldn't see his face, but his voice sounded different than usual.

"What has happened?"

"I spoke with the staff and they insist the line be repaired immediately. They asked me who was responsible for telephone connections with the infantry. I gave them your name and was told that you, yourself, must go and repair that line."

I sat up, wondering just what was going on. "But they have the radio for emergency and the new line will be ready in the morning!"

"I'm sorry, Sergei, but it's an order," he said in a low tone.

"Who ordered it?" I asked quickly.

"He looked the other way and answered, "I don't know. It came from staff."

I stood there a few seconds while my heart pounded, thinking just who ordered me to go out there.

"All right, I'll go." There was nothing else to do but obey orders.

"I'll go with you as far as the infantry trenches and help you all I can," my Captain said quietly.

"Thank you, but I'll go alone. No one can help me."

I took the necessary tools and looked at the Captain who was looking at the ground. "Farewell, Comrade Captain."

"I'll see you later," he answered and we shook hands.

There I was again, in the infantry trenches. Obviously, the Germans didn't know what the Russians were after, but they certainly tried to find out, as they continued to send up flares and shots at random, periodically. I stood there, looking out into space; it seemed to me I saw the body of our telephone man. Beside him there had to be a hole made by the shell-fire. If I could run up to this hole just after a light flare, as the second man tried to do, I might make it. But how will I find the ends of the wire, tape them together and get back? Then again, how could I run up to that hole while the Germans were shouting even now, when nobody is out there? I am dead, I thought. No one can help me now.

I clearly imagined how I would run and after several steps fall, riddled with shots. I felt cold and hot at the same time. My throat was dry and my feet were numb. Then, suddenly, I heard myself whispering, "Our Father ... " I don't know how I remembered it, but I mixed all the words and sentences, and added my own words. For the first time in my life I prayed—the best I knew how. I knew that only He could help me now.

I was still praying when I noted a soldier, one of the infantrymen, who was sitting on the ground in the trench, watching me and, it seemed, smiling at me ironically. Embarrassed, I turned back and began to climb out of the trench. In the next moment someone stopped me from behind and said, "Hey, take it easy!" Astonished, I turned around and saw the soldier behind me. But he didn't smile.

"Where are you going, my Son?" he asked, omitting my title. "Wait a moment. From there, one does not return."

I looked at him. He was an ordinary Russian, about in his fifties, a peasant, probably. His face was kind and calm and his voice inspired trust. Forgetting my groundless embarrassment of a few minutes before, I told him about my order and my fear. We sat down on the ground and he listened carefully. Then he said, slowly, "Well, I see you are in trouble. Listen to me, my Son. Do you know what is down this hill? It's a small river, more like a brook. If you will go on the right, along the trenches, you will find a place where the Germans are not throwing light flares. There you will come to the brook. Wade into the water. It isn't too deep. Follow the brook to the place where your wire is broken, being careful that only your head is above water. The Germans can't see down there, but in case some of them come down to the water, make sure they can't see you. Now, when you get to the place you may find a little more difficulty. I think you will be all right, my Son. Are you afraid?"

"Yes, I am."

"And when you helped your wounded man a short while ago, were you afraid?"

"I don't know. Everything happened so fast ... "

"All right, Son, go now," he shoved me forward. "Down there is the brook. God will be with you."

I found everything exactly as the old soldier had told me. I waded through the water and arrived at the place where the wire was broken. The rockets brightened the sky above me and with their help I could clearly see both ends of the wire. A few seconds of darkness and I had the wire mended. I returned to the trench by the same route I had come, happy as I had never been before, and dripping wet. I began to look for the soldier, but couldn't find him anywhere. I walked along the trenches and looked at every one of them; some were asleep; some sitting and smoking, but the old man wasn't among them. I hadn't asked his name and all those men were so much alike; unshaven, tired Russian soldiers. My Captain came down to see where I was and found me searching the faces of the soldiers. He knew the line was in order and was wondering why I didn't come back.

I returned to my own trench where my men waited for me with several bottles of vodka and we had a great celebration there in our underground trench. Later they told me that I was very drunk and told many absurd stories. They said I tried to teach our Captain to pray "Our Father," and I requested them all to be very quiet while I talked. I also told them about a soldier who was like a God, but who was dressed like a Russian soldier.

XXI

Our troops were following the retreating enemy as we were advancing slowly through a forest with our infantry ahead of us. As I rode with my men I was suddenly called to the regiment staff at the rear of the column. There I learned that the infantry had radioed that they noted a few enemy tanks in the forest behind a hill. I was ordered to reconnoitre and report the position of those tanks. Our column stopped in the forest while I took one man with me and rode forward. The Commisar and an officer followed us, and at the edge of the forest the Commisar pointed to a hill to our left.

"Those enemy tanks should be there just over the hill. If our column had continued its way out of the forest all our artillery could have been wrecked in a few minutes," he said to me.

"All right, Comrade Commisar, we'll climb that other hill from where we can see them. I'll radio you their position in about half an hour."

"Half an hour? What are you talking about, Lieutenant?" and he glared at me. "You will ride straight up the hill and establish their position right away. Give us the signal with the rocket pistol. Do it in five minutes!" he commanded and continued to glare.

"But Comrade Commisar," I countered, "it is an open space, the Germans can shoot us in one minute."

"Maybe," he said very calmly, "but we will know where the tanks are," and he turned away.

I didn't dare say another word because he could report me for refusing an order. I whipped my horse and rode up the hill, the soldier following. Half way up, I ordered the soldier to dismount and hide in the shelter of some bushes. I rode forward alone. Every second I expected machine gun volleys from the top of the hill, but nothing happened. I began to think there were no tanks at all. I rode on up to the top and came face to face with two German tanks about a hundred feet from me.

In a flash I saw the surprised faces of the tank men as they stared at me. But in the next second the covers of the tanks were closed and machine guns began to turn in my direction. My horse kept racing on toward the tanks and I, surprised too, didn't try to turn him back. There wasn't time to even think of turning back. I struck my horse and we galloped between the two tanks and continued to race further. Suddenly the horse stopped. In front of us was a deep chasm; the horse saw it and stopped so quickly that he threw me from the saddle. I rolled down the hill. In that moment I heard a volley over my head and my horse stumbled down beside me, dying. I wasn't hurt too badly and at once fired my rocket. Then I ran toward the bushes to hide, but it wasn't necessary as the tanks started their motors and began to come down from the hill. It was a futile move because they had to go past an open area, downhill, where our artillery was already waiting for them. In a few minutes the tanks were hit and burst into flames. We captured several surviving Germans.

When I got back to my regiment, without my horse, the men wanted to embrace me and shake my hand. The Commisar only looked at me and said, "You see, I told you it would be all right."

I didn't answer him. The soldiers stood there, looking at the ground.

At that time I failed to realize the real meaning of these orders, which were given me by the Commisar. This officer, ranking as a Captain, was responsible for the political discipline and Communist propaganda in the regiment. However, as the head of the Communist cell he was the most powerful man in the regiment headquarters. Even the Commandant of the regiment, a Colonel, was obliged to listen to his advice and proposals in purely military matters. Of course, very often this advice and counsel were absolutely inexpert as the Commisar had very little military training—his education had been mostly political—but everyone had to accept his word.

I didn't suspect that there was any connection between this dangerous mission and my **Personal Characteristics** which were included in my dossier. Every officer's personal dossier was in the Commisar's file, sent to the regiment at the same time the officer was. The dossier included the man's general history, especially his political affiliation. Of course, no one could know all that might be in his dossier. Probably in mine was the history of my father's political ideas, his arrest and death, also my mother's arrest and our forced trip to Siberia.

As my assignments became more and more dangerous I tried to explain to myself that it could only be a coincidence that the Commisar sent me on so many of them; he probably simply didn't know how to handle those military matters. However, a certain doubt entered my mind again and again as to whether it was really only a coincidence.

XXII

A few days after we crossed the Hungarian border, the Germans retreated, trying to stop our advance in every possible way. I was given the order to establish a reconnoitering point on a hill and to help our infantry with artillery fire. I chose two men and we approached the hill through a thick forest. From the top of the hill we would be able to see the Germans' positions. But they were wise and kept this hill under constant artillery fire to prevent us from using it for reconnaissance. I decided to climb up the hill anyway to discover the enemy's main positions. My men muttered their discontent, but crawled behind me, jumping from one bomb-made hole to another. I found it was impossible to reach the top of the hill as the bombs exploded around it continually. I could see the ruins of a house on the top, very near us, but there was an open space between us and the house. The Germans noted our movements and kept this space under heavy machine gun fire.

"Let's go back while we can," suggested one of the men. I shrugged my shoulders; what else could we do? But suddenly I heard something entirely foreign to a battle ground.

"Did you hear it?" I asked the men, not believing my ears.

"What?" they asked. "What did you hear, Lieutenant?"

"Crying. The cry of a child. Don't you hear it? Are you deaf? A child must be in that house," I yelled.

"No, I can't hear anything," one of them answered.

"Now! Again! I heard it again! There is a child in that house, I am sure!"

"All right, Lieutenant, maybe you're right, maybe a Hungarian or German child is there, but what can we do about it? We can't get there. You can see for yourself."

"But we must. We must do something about it. We can't just go away and let him die—even if it is a German child. But how?" I shouted, desperately looking at the ruined house. "Wait a minute, I have an idea!" I started looking at my watch while listening to the heavy explosions of the bombs.

"Listen to me, men. After every four explosions there is a little interruption—very short, but just enough time for us to get there, if we run very fast."

"But the machine guns, Lieutenant, they will cut us down. We could never make it."

"Yes, if they should see us; but if the last explosion happened to be on the left side of us, they would not see us on account of the dust that will lift between them and us!"

Seeing they were not in sympathy with my plan, I said, "All right, boys, you stay here. I'll go alone."

They looked at each other. "We'll go with you, Lieutenant," one of them said simply.

We put down all heavy and unnecessary equipment, excepting the radio and began to wait and count.

"Now!" I ordered, and we ran, ran as never before in our lives. I don't know how, but we got there alive.

"It is there, Lieutenant, I hear the voice plainly, there," a soldier pointed to a cellar door, which was nearly covered with stones and rubble. We tore at the trash surrounding the door while the bombs exploded near us with deafening noise. Fragments whistled past our heads, but we neither saw nor heard anything but the weak voice in front of us. At last we got the door open enough to crawl into the cellar on all fours. The child was there under a beam which hung dangerously near. Beside him, two feet jutted out from under a pile of rocks, probably the mother's. She was dead. I took the child in my arms, a little boy about a year old. He stopped crying and smiled at three dirty faces looking down at him. We looked at each other and started to laugh.

"One of you stay here with the baby and one come with me."

Outside I could easily locate the artillery positions and in a short time our artillery received the directions. As our first shells started to explode near the German positions, they knew they were discovered. Their fire was broken off and they retreated in haste. Our infantry continued their advance.

"All right, Lieutenant, what shall we do with him?" asked one of the men as he awkwardly held the child in his arms.

"I guess the best thing to do is to take him to the nearest village, where the Germans have just left. I saw them leaving through the binoculars. Maybe some of this little fellow's relatives live in that village."

I relieved the soldier of the child and he seemed glad to be rid of him. We walked down to where we had tied our horses and started to ride toward the village. I think we must have made a funny-looking parade, a Russian officer on horseback holding a small child in his arms, and two rough soldiers following, riding into a Hungarian village. From the expressions on the faces of some of the people we passed, I guess they will never forget the entry of the Russian army into their village.

Not knowing their language, it was difficult to explain where and how we found the child; but as I expected, relatives were found, and they proved to be the grandparents. They tried to tell us something, but I could only make out that they were thanking us, shaking our hands with tears in their eyes. We tried to tell them in our language, "It was really nothing; don't mention it."

We gave them the baby and our unusual mission was accomplished.

I ordered the two soldiers not to mention this affair to anyone, but after a short time it must have leaked out. I noticed conversation sometimes stopped as soon as I appeared, and a few times I caught the words, "our midwife," but it was all in good humor and with respect—I let it pass.

XXIII

I went through the usual duties of an officer of the Russian army and each day took me to a new town or village, all through Rumania, Hungary and Yugoslavia, where I saw and heard things I had never known before. First, I noticed the houses, little houses, no huts. Each family seemed to have its own house and plot of ground with trees and gardens growing. There were very few apartment houses compared with Russian towns.

Then I noticed how well the people were dressed, in spite of the war. They wore beautiful clothes and each person wore many bright colors. I couldn't help remembering how Mother was dressed; dark, drab clothes exactly like all the other women, no individuality, almost like uniforms, excepting the ruling class whom we practically never saw. When they whisked by in their large, powerful cars, we could see bright colors flashing by. We could not even see these clothes in the stores, as the ration cards we were given did not allow us even to enter the doors of the better stores. We could only buy in the stores set aside for workers.

I noticed nearly everyone rode a bicycle. None of my friends and schoolmates had bicycles though we often talked about how we would try to get one, even knowing it was impossible.

In one small city where we were billeted for a few days, I saw one of my men disassembling a bicycle, in the hope of taking it home with him after the war was over. It was impossible to send it home; we couldn't send anything. I remember how he carefully saved every nut and bolt, even taking down notes on how to reassemble it once he got it home. I never knew whether he made it or not.

Many of the homes I saw had radios and record players. I had seen and heard them in Leningrad and had worked with radio in training school, but to have one in a home was new to me.

Our men bought up and picked up all the wrist watches they could find. I had never owned a watch, but soon after our first fight at the front, one of my men brought me a watch which he took away from a war prisoner. A watch was a luxury a Russian worker could not have. The shoes and uniforms of the soldiers of these European countries were very much better than those of my own men.

In the cities where we drove the Germans out, I noticed that in the apartment houses, almost every apartment had its own bathroom and kitchen. In Leningrad there was one kitchen and one bathroom, toilet only, for each floor. All families on that floor were obliged to use these accommodations. I thought of Mother. How wonderful it would be for her to have her own kitchen and her own bath tub, where on could bathe leisurely at night and then go to bed. How much easier her life could be.

XXIV

The biggest puzzle of all was where were the masses of famished workers, the slaves of Capitalism, that I had been told about? It had been drummed into us over and over again that we, the Russians, with our Communist ideology, were to be the saviors of the world. We would relieve starvation and misery among the workers, bring them out of the depths of poverty and up to our own level, making everything better for all.

Instead of misery I found these people of Europe much better off than the Russians had ever been in my time. I began to feel that everything I had been taught was lies, lies, lies, and to make matters worse, there was no one I could talk with about all this. Once a fellow officer made a reference to better conditions than we had at home, but I very quickly pretended to see an old friend across the street, and made a quick getaway. It was not safe to listen as he might be spying on me; how could I know? I began to understand why some of our older soldiers had been sent to the rear and new men sent to the front. I'm sure they were afraid we would learn too much about other ways of life than ours, and become dissatisfied.

I found compulsory, free education for all. Compulsory! Free! Again I was reminded of the poster that hung on the wall in my school room. "You must study and study and study." Signed by Lenin. And once more the picture passed through my mind—and this time with much greater force—of the teacher reading off the names of those who must leave because they couldn't pay. I relived again how we, the students, looked at the teacher, who returned our stare with a frozen face and turned and walked out of the room. The rejected ones followed the teacher, my best friend Boris among them. I never saw him again but sometimes later heard that he had been sent with others to a sort of barracks-boarding school where he would learn a trade. We were both fifteen years old. The reliving of this picture brought new agony to my tortured, mixed-up thinking.

The people of these European cities where we drove the enemy out were glad to see the Germans leave, but they did not want to see the Russian army moving in. This was very depressing to us, even crushing, because we thought we brought liberty and a better way of life to the slaves of European Capitalists. Again—where were these slaves we were supposed to bring so much happiness to?

I must admit I was ashamed of the bad manners displayed by some of my fellow officers in restaurants and other public places. Often they were drunk, rude and even violent, and it was very unpleasant to overhear remarks from the natives about the actions of the Russian soldiers. Whenever I witnessed the crude manners of some of my own men I thanked my wonderful mother who had taught me better.

As a schoolboy studying world history and geography, my friends and I often talked about the day when we would join the navy and see some of the countries we read about. As for traveling the world on our own, that was impossible. Even if one could get a permit, there was never enough money for traveling. Only the ruling class was allowed to travel and even they were checked very thoroughly before they were given a permit, and on returning, naturally told only what the government bodies wanted them to relate. I never knew anyone who had seen any other country other than Russia, even though Finland was just across the bay from Leningrad.

But now we were here, in Europe, whether our leaders wanted it or not. We didn't need to listen to them about the life abroad any more. We could see it with our own eyes, and we saw it!

XXV

One day in Hungary in September, 1944 we stopped near a little town to rest and eat. Our infantry had passed through a short time before and their reconnoitering party informed us the Germans had withdrawn in great haste. After our poor meal, my Captain and a sergeant and I rode off into town to look around a little. The place was absolutely empty, the inhabitants having fled, probably thinking there would be a big battle right in the town.

We dismounted and my friends found what they were looking for—a wine cellar with several barrels of wine. We sat down to drink, but after a few drinks, I thought I'd go upstairs to the kitchen to look for some food. The house was clean and very pleasantly furnished. But there was no food. They must have taken it with them. I looked around a little more and saw a bookcase. I took out some books from force of habit. I couldn't read a word of Hungarian, but suddenly I noticed several books in Russian. Chekov. Tolstoy. Turgenev. I had read all of them before, but, what is this? I read the title: Novi Zavjet.* Yes, I held a Bible in my hands, just like the one my mother had guarded so carefully. I stood there holding the book and it seemed as if my mother were putting it into my hands. I felt as if she were with me now, as the Bible was an inseparable part of my mother. Different pictures passed before my eyes. I saw Mother with the book in her hands as she read me some of the stories. There was my father also, sitting by the big stove in our room. I recalled another time, later when I was attending school. Mother handed me her Bilbe and said, "Now that you have learned to read, you can read this too."

"But, Mother, why should I? This book is all about God, a lot of fairy tales. There is no God!"

I saw again how she looked at me. Then she glanced at my

---

*New Testament

father and sorrowfully, without a word, put the book away in the chest. I saw her in the cattle car with the Bible in her hands. I heard her voice, "Don't forget Him and He will be with you always, Sergei."

"Sergei, Sergei," someone called more and more loudly until I realized where I was. My friends in the wine cellar were calling me. Quickly I put the Bible in my pocket and joined them down below. "Did you find anything?"

"Yes, I did. No, I mean I didn't. There's no food up there."

"Then let's go back." We took several bottles and returned to our regiment.

I put the Bible in my pack when no one was looking and waited for the time when I could read secretly, but found no opportunity until everyone was asleep. I lighted a candle and lying on the ground covered with straw, I began to read. Around me in the trench my soldiers slept; but in case someone awakened and saw I was reading, I kept a newspaper near. How I wished I had read this book when my mother gave it to me. Forgive me, my dear mother, for the pain I brought to your heart so many times when I refused to listen to you.

I remembered hearing Mother read to me on our Christmas: "And she brought forth her first-born son, and wrapped him in swaddling clothes and laid him in a manger; because there was no room in the Inn."

I read the book to the end and then read it over and over and discovered things which amazed me: truth, justice and love to one's fellow man. I read this book every chance I had, and I felt as if I were a different person, as if I had discovered a new world. Sometimes I was afraid, wondering if He would forgive me for all I had done against Him, but I read in my Bible the answer which gave me the hope to believe He would: "I say unto you, that likewise joy shall be in heaven over one sinner that repenteth, more than over ninety and nine just persons which need no repentance."

I learned the philosophy of Jesus Christ taught only goodness. There was no hatred. I discovered the Ten Commandments were just and humane, but the Communist rule denied this. Why?

I continued to read every time I could steal away. Gradually all I had been taught began to crumble, as if a slow earthquake were shaking everything down from the mountains. I began to view the world with other eyes—the world in which I found myself.

One night while reading secretly I came across something that really opened my eyes. It was in the book of Mathew, Chapter

7, Verses 13-14.

"Enter ye in at the strait gate: for wide is the gate, and broad is the way, that leadeth to destruction, and many there be which go in there at:

"Because strait is the gate, and narrow is the way, which leadeth unto life, and few there be that find it."

These words seemed to have a message just for me. Reading these verses was like looking into the mirror of truth.

In a Hungarian village I saw Crucifixes, one at the entrance of the town and one at the end. At the last one I dismounted a little beyond the Crucifix and pretending to fix my saddle, waited until the last of our men disappeared around the bend in the road. Then I approached the Crucifix. There was no one near and I took off my red starred cap and stood there looking at the image of the Son of God. "They can no more destroy Christ now than they did when they crucified Him." I remembered the words, but who said them? I couldn't remember. Maybe, but yes—it was my mother who said them as we looked at the ruined Russian church.

Sometime later I received a letter from my mother:

> "My dear Son, I received the letter you wrote me from Hungary. I was astonished at the unusual tone—it was so unknown and new to me as if you had not written it. I felt that something had happened to you, some change in your life which has made you happy. But later I understood all, my Son. You wrote, "Mother, I have found spiritual peace. Yes, you were right—and I haven't forgotten anything, and that you said to me, 'Fight bravely, my Son.' And now I am very happy because of it. I knew it always. Who knows you better than your mother?"

I knew Mother would understand my letter which I wrote very carefully because of censorship. "Fight bravely" was for the censor.

I went from one country to another and saw in each place, despite the war, life was much better and the people happier than in Russia. I was obsessed with the idea; I dreamed about it and began to be afraid I might talk in my sleep. By this time I was certain all I had been told about Europe's capitalist system was a pack of lies, and this knowledge shook me to my very roots. I didn't want to believe it. I wanted to crawl back into my shell, my Russia, my homeland. The more I thought, the more I searched in every town and village for some sign of starving slaves, but I could find none. I concluded that we, the Russians, were the slaves, slaves to the Communist system. We lived with no freedom of thought, with barely enough to eat and in fear, afraid of being sent to the Siberian waste lands to slave the rest of our life.

I knew at last I could never go back to Russia. This decision hurt, with a deep-down hurt. I couldn't think it possible that I was going to turn my back on my own country, my Mother Russia. I wanted to hide my face. I hated myself. I wanted to die, but I knew I could never go back.

XXVI

In November of 1944 our regiment reached the River Danube in Hungary, near the little town of Mohach. The enemy was on the other side trying to utilize the river as a barrier that would stop our advance. Of course, all bridges were demolished, so our engineering units started to build a pontoon bridge. But the Germans bombarded us so heavily that all our attempts to build a bridge were destroyed in the beginning! It was impossible to find the positions of the enemy's artillery from our side of the river during such a short time, and they were hidden perfectly, indeed.

In the meantime, however, our troops to the right of us had managed to build a pontoon bridge and cross the river. It meant that if the Germans on our front had not begun to retreat quickly, they would be completely surrounded by the next day. All we had to do now was wait. It didn't happen that way, at least not for me.

A soldier came to me saying that I was wanted on the telephone, someone from the staff was calling me.

"Lieutenant Sazonov?" It was the Commisar himself. "Take one or two soldiers and a radio. Take a pontoon boat. There's a heavy fog on the river now, so cross at once and report the exact positions of the enemy's artillery!"

"But Comrade... " I tried to speak to him but the phone was dead on the other end. The order had been given and I had to execute it, even though it meant suicide. Every attempt to cross the river at this point had been paid with men's lives. All boats and rafts were destroyed by precise German artillery and machine gun fire. True, there was a heavy fog enveloping the river, but it wasn't a stable one, a wind scattered it periodically. And, why did the Commisar want to send men to their death when it wasn't necessary? A great doubt entered my heart, but I had no time to think about it. The radio man and I (I didn't want to take two men) went to the river where several pontoon boats were sheltered. I turned away where my soldier couldn't see me and prayed "Our Father." I had learned this prayer only a few months before though I remembered hearing Mother say it many times alone in her room.

We sat down in the boat and began to row very fast toward the other side of the river. Around and above us was nothing but thick fog and below the cold gray water, and for all our fast rowing we made very slow progress as we had to fight a strong downstream current. It seemed that we could not reach the other side. I hoped the fog would never lift, but a moment later my hopes and wishes came to nothing as the wind came up suddenly and in a flash our boat was without protection of the fog. In front of us was the enemy's bank. A few yards behind us was the protecting fog.

"Go back!" I ordered, but it was too late. They had seen us. I heard the fire of machine guns and bullets whistled all around us. We jumped into the river, and at once I turned on my back and let the current carry me downstream, then I dived under. When I came up I was in the fog again. I didn't know what happened to my soldier after I saw him swimming toward the protective fog bank, while the bullets were falling all around us.

Now in the fog I began to swim very fast because the water was very cold and my body was becoming stiff. My high boots were too heavy and dragged me down and the uniform was cumbersome. I knew I would never be able to swim to our bank, but I kept going with all the strength I had. Suddenly I saw something dark in front of me, and I automatically extended my hands. I couldn't believe it, but I held in my hands a branch of a shrub which grew on solid ground. I couldn't understand it, but climbed out of the water and a little later I discovered I was on a small island in the middle of the river where a few shrubs and trees grew. It meant I could save my life if I could get to the mainland before the fog lifted. I hurriedly took off my heavy wet clothes and fastened them with my belt to a small log. Then I began to jump like a wild horse in order to get my blood circulating again. I plunged into the river, pushing the log in front of me. I cannot describe how I ever swam across that river. It was terrible. With every stroke I thanked my father and brother for teaching me to swim when I was a child.

The current carried me far downstream from my regiment. Coming out of the water I began to run along the bank of the river, as fast as I could. But, toward the end, I could hardly walk. I felt very sick. When my Captain saw me he immediately sent me to the regiment's hospital.

The next day the Captain visited me there. What he told me

secretly that day opened my eyes, and I began to understand many things which had happened to me.

"Listen to me carefully," he whispered. "You saved my life once, Sergei. Now I will try to do something for you which I think may be very important in your future. I really shouldn't do this; I could be shot for it. I am a Communist, you know, but I feel that I must tell you this. You are in the black book. Your political characteristics are very unfavorable. I know because the Commisar once mentioned it at a party meeting."

He straightened up and lit a cigarette, then leaned down over my bed again and whispered the same as before. "But things more serious than that have happened. After we entered Rumania they spied on you. They had their men among your soldiers and a book was found in your bag. I don't know what it was but the Commisar was surprised about it. They found it while you were out on some action ... "

"I'll tell you what it was. It was a Bible," I whispered.

"They saw you when you prayed in front of a crucifix, and saw you make the sign of the cross before going into action. They know that you talked with civilians about life in Rumania, Yugoslavia and Hungary and they know about some of the remarks you made to some of our soldiers."

I said nothing because it was the truth.

"You remember," he continued, "when in Rumania this Commisar sent you on a very dangerous mission against German tanks? When he, the Commisar, and one of his men passed me, I heard him say, 'It wouldn't be a great loss for us.' They were talking about you, Sergei. I don't know what will happen to you, but you know yourself what it all means. I don't wish to advise you. You know what to do. But I think I have paid my debt to you. I wish you luck," and he went out as quickly as he had come.

XXVII

The next morning the doctor came in and remarked briefly, "You have a pretty bad case of pneumonia, Lieutenant, and we're not equipped to care for you properly here. You will be transferred to our hospital in Beograd where you'll have a better chance for recovery. Besides that, our regiment is moving forward today. You will be moved at once. Good-bye."

He finished his hurried message and was gone. Two men came in to help me onto a stretcher.

It was late in November the day I was put in the ambulance to go to Beograd. This improvised ambulance—really only a truck with rough shelves built in it—was not conducive to sightseeing so I saw almost nothing of the Yugoslav country. I was too sick to care anyway, but I did notice a big pontoon bridge across the Danube near a city called Novi-Sad.

After a long day in this rough-riding, made-over truck, we arrived in Beograd late in the evening and were taken to a large hospital in a suburb of the city. A part of the building had been taken over for a Russian military hospital. The medical personnel was Russian, but some of the nurses were Yugoslavs.

I was put in a room with three other Russians, none of them so ill that they were obliged to stay in bed all of the time. Two of them were privates and the third was a much older man. I wondered about him as he was very quiet and seemed to me a rather strange person. The doctors addressed him as "Colonel Sokolov," but he addressed the doctors as "Gospodin"* instead of the usual "Comrade Doctor." This, among other differences in his speech and behavior piqued my curiosity.

At the first opportunity I asked one of my neighbors about

*Sir or Mister

this strange colonel.

"That one? Well, his name, as I suppose you know, is Sokolov. He is an ex-colonel of the Kingdom of Yugoslavia—a White Russian who escaped from Russia after the revolution of 1917."

"What? A White Guardsman? Here in our hospital? Why?"

"Well, I think he deserves it, Comrade Lieutenant. He saved several of our soldiers from death."

"He?" I was more than ever surprised. "He is supposed to be our enemy—every ex-Czarist is the enemy of our people!"

The soldier gave me a long searching look. "You won't believe it, Comrade Lieutenant, but I saw it with my own eyes. It happened here in Beograd when we had some street fights with the Germans as they retreated from the city. I was among a group of about fifteen soldiers who advanced carefully along a street, but we failed to see a squad of Germans who were hiding behind a broken down wall. He, Colonel Sokolov, noted the Germans from his apartment window. 'Back! Back! Germans on the left of you! Back!'

"Of course we found shelter or simply dropped to the ground. The Germans started to shoot. Several of us were wounded, Colonel Sokolov also. So he is here now in our hospital. Our regiment Commander thanked him personally."

It was a new experience for me. We were taught in Russia that all White refugees from Russia were mortal enemies of our people. They wished to restore Czarism. We were told that these imigrants were fighting along with the Germans against us.

I was very anxious to speak with this Colonel Sokolov. I wanted to hear about his life in old Russia, particularly about the revolution. I knew all about it from the Communists' point of view; and now I would like to hear the other side of the story, but it was impossible to ask such questions. We weren't alone. Always one, or the other, or both of the soldiers were in the room. We talked many times but never mentioned political events in connection with Communism.

One day, however, both of the soldiers were out of the room at the same time and I decided to ask him about his life in Russia.

"Well, Lieutenant," he answered, looking at me thoughtfully, "do you wish to know the whole truth, or ... "

"Please, Sir, only the truth. I am not a Communist, Sir, and I have reason to believe that many of their practices would bear looking in to."

"I think I can trust you, young man," he remarked slowly, "and of course you know what would happen to me if some of your special people were to discover that I, a White Guardsman, was disturbing your convictions."

I nodded.

"So this means that I may count on your absolute discretion, Lieutenant?"

"Yes, indeed, Sir, and may I ask the same of you?"

We shook hands.

He began by telling me about his family and their life in Russia.

"My father was a school teacher and we lived in a small town. Lived very modestly, I might add ... "

"Your father was a teacher?" I interrupted, surprised.

"Yes, a teacher. Why does that surprise you?"

"I was told that all refugees were rich men—landlords, property owners, Czarist officers, big merchants and the like," I answered.

"Well, you have been misinformed because a large percentage of imigrants did not belong to rich families. I can name you many of my friends in Beograd who escaped from Russia not because they were rich or because they belonged to the Czarist regime. No. They ran away from their motherland because of Bolshevik Tyranny."

I was confused and didn't know what to think about it. The Colonel continued to tell me his story about his life in Russia and especially about World War I and the beginning of the revolution. I didn't interrupt him too often, rather I listened as carefully as I could to every word he spoke.

After a few hours of our conversation I noticed the Colonel began to tire, so I asked no more questions that day. He seemed to need rest, so I pretended to fall asleep.

But there was no sleep for me. I reviewed in my mind all Colonel Sokolov had said, but all my old views and convictions which had been implanted by the long years of Communist propaganda had very deep roots and I said to myself: "Be careful, Sergei. Don't believe every word he is saying. He can be an honest man but his interpretation of facts could be an incorrect one because of his Czarist ideology." However, the reality that he risked his life to help our soldiers didn't permit me to believe that he was an enemy of the Russian people.

Little by little I came to trust him, realizing that he was a very learned and intelligent gentleman with honest and logical points of view on historical events. My side of our conversations was us-

usally listening and questioning. I told him nothing of my father's death, nor of Mother's and my trip to Siberia. I didn't mention my very bad war experiences, or finding the Bible and my consequent change of heart; but one day he asked me if I believed in the existence of God. I hesitated then answered, "Yes." I saw that he wasn't surprised, though he didn't comment.

One day while we were alone he remarked, "It's odd, isn't it? You, Sergei, fight now against Germany as I did twenty years ago. You will have victory now, no question about that. We could have had it also if Lenin hadn't destroyed our army."

"How do you mean, Lenin destroyed ... ?"

"How? Very simple. Lenin had been living in exile in Switzerland for some time. The Germans gave him plenty of money and sent him to Russia in a sealed car all the way across Germany and Poland into St. Petersburg. He had an agreement to destroy the Russian army and he did it."

"Why, Colonel, Sir, I can't believe it. It's incredible!" I exclaimed excitedly.

"Well, it's all true, Son," he answered in a quiet voice and continued, "The Germans wanted a separate treaty with Russia so they could finish the war at least on that one front. They knew that Lenin, with his revolutionary ideas and with German money, could upset the whole Russian army."

"But," I interjected, "we in Russia were told that it was all imperialist propaganda. I remember hearing about it in school when I was a child. All this about the sealed car from Switzerland, very dramatic, but all a fabrication of the Capitalists. Nobody believed it."

"No, Son, it is a fact. You will find it in a good many histories. I see what you are thinking. All right, I'll have a friend of mine bring a few books here to me and you can read for yourself. These will be recognized authors, translations from English and French to Yugoslavian. You'll understand them, but I will give you a dictionary, too. Anyway, you know, it's very much like Russian."

I received the books a few days later and read them, secretly, of course. I found that Colonel Sokolov was right about the Lenin case and about many other historical things about which he had told me.

"And this, your uniform, your epaulets, almost the same as I wore when I was a Russian Lieutenant. I have photographs at home of myself in that uniform and on account of these epaulets I was supposed to be shot."

"You? Shot? Why?"

Sitting in our hospital beds alone for the time being and hoping no one would come in and interrupt us, the Colonel talked and I listened in open-mouthed wonder, as he gradually told me a history of my country I had never heard before.

"Why?" in answer to my question, "because I was an officer. I will explain. It happened after November 7, 1917, when the Bolsheviks pulled down the Provisional Government of Kerensky and took over. Lenin and his Bolsheviks gave the order to our army's commander to stop the fighting because Russia (in fact the Bolsheviks) would negotiate a separate armistice with Germany.

"General Duhonin refused the order because Russia had an alliance with England, France and later with the United States against Germany, the same as they have at the present time. Can you imagine what would happen if now, Hitler sent someone like Lenin to destroy your army? Or if England and U.S.A. would try to negotiate a separate peace with Germany?"

"But what happened when General Duhonin refused to obey the order?"

"What happened? The Bolsheviks sent their political agitators into the army and these agitators began to work on the soldiers. 'You've had enough war! You're tired of war! The Bolshevik government wants peace. They want you to go home, but your officers are against it. They want to continue the war. Kill your officers! Kill them! They are your enemies—these officers—enemies of the soldiers and the people of Russia. Kill them!'

"And the soldiers began to kill officers. They lynched General Duhonin and several of his officers. Some of us escaped. I was one of the lucky ones—with the help of some of my soldiers I got away.

"I was a young Lieutenant and believed and obeyed my commanders the same as you do today. Have you ever thought your soldiers would shoot you because you are an officer?"

"No, I have never had any such thought. I get along very well with my men. We feel a certain fellowship."

"No, I couldn't imagine it either at that time, but the Bolsheviks put out such powerful arguments in their propaganda that a great many men did kill their officers. Lenin did his work well, I must say."

We were interrupted by nurses coming in and out doing their work about the hospital, bandages for the Colonel and medicines for me. It seemed the doctor was right when he sent me to this hospital in Beograd, as I had a very bad case of pneumonia, and sometimes these long conversations, eager as I was to listen, were very tiring.

The next day, however, we were able to continue and Colonel Sokolov's first remark was, "Did you ever hear—no, I don't think you did—what happened in Brest-Litovsk in March, 1918?"

"Well, I knew that in Brest-Litovsk Russia and Germany negotiated for peace between them. It was necessary for the Bolsheviks to stop the war with Germany; but why are you asking?"

"Yes, then I'm sure you know the Bolsheviks paid for that peace with a huge piece of our Russian territory—we lost Poland, Finland, all Baltic provinces and Bessarabia?"

"But they were forced by the Germans," I interrupted.

"Certainly, but Germany could do this because the Bolsheviks were destroying the Russian army, and the Germans could dictate the terms of that 'treaty.' It was a terrible thing to give our territory in order to get power in the hands of the Bolsheviks. Can you imagine if, for example, England's Labor Party giving English territory in order to grab the ruling power?"

"Yes, I understand your feeling, Sir, but do you wish to tell me that the Czar's regime was a good one for Russia and the Russian people?"

"Oh, no, Sergei, I don't defend the Czar. No. I am only trying to explain a few facts about the revolution because I see you have been misinformed and I know why. Believe me, the revolution was not the deed of Bolsheviks, it was the result of the Czar's administration. You wonder? Yes, it was the Czar's regime with bad governing, the long unsuccessful war, and poverty widespread in the country. The Bolsheviks simply took advantage of the people's revolt against the Czar and used it for snatching the power in their hands.

"This is how it started: It was in November, 1916, in Petrograd (Leningrad now). Hungry people marched in the streets in the snow, led by a priest, and asking only for food. The police fired on them. The written order for firing was signed by Czar Nicholas. The next day, as the result of this firing, the whole city was full of rebellious people and hundreds of thousands of soldiers who refused to obey their officers and joined the people. It was a spontaneous riot of the people against the Czar. The police force dispersed and there was no authority. The people asked the abdication of the Czar. The Duma,* which had no power in the time of the Czar, also demanded it. Even the army chiefs asked for abdication of the Czar; which, as you know, took place on March 16, 1917."

"Where were the Bolsheviks at that time?" I asked

"Lenin arrived in Petrograd in April, 1917 and Trotsky arrived from America some time later. After the Czar's abdication, labor leader Kerenski formed a so-called "Provisional Government" which was the very first democratic government in Russia, but he decided to continue the war against Germany, as Russia was in alliance with England, France and the United States. And this was the reason why the Germans needed Lenin—to stop the war against them.

"On November 7, the Bolsheviks, under Lenin's and Trotsky's leadership, promised the end of the war to the soldiers, peasants and workers. The Bolsheviks captured the "Provisional Government" and took over all power in their hands. On that date, November 7, 1917, Communist Russia was born."

I wanted time to think about these things Colonel Sokolov told me. It was just like a university class, where I might be sitting, listening to the instructor, but I wasn't, I was in a hospital bed, trying to recover from pneumonia. He had told me things that opened my eyes dispelling some of the confusion that had lived with me the last two years—years of doubt and inner struggle. Unfortunately, that was our last conversation in the hospital. The next day, for some military reason, all of us Russian soldiers were transferred to another hospital in the city of Subotica. Colonel Sokolov was disappointed about this as, of course, it didn't include him, and I was very sorry as I had grown fond of the Colonel. I looked on him as though he were my father and I admired him very much. But there was nothing we could do about it so he gave me his home address in Beograd with an invitation to visit him as soon as I was well. We parted as two old friends.

The evening of that same day I, with several others, was driven to Subotica where we arrived early the next morning.

---

*Russian Parliament

XXVIII

Subotica is a city in Yugoslavia near the Hungarian border with a population of about one hundred thousand Serbs, Croatians and Hungarians. The hospital was located in a school building and filled with wounded and sick soldiers.

I was put through a thorough examination and the doctors remarked that the long overnight trip in the rough ambulance hadn't helped my pneumonia any and that I could expect to be hospitalized for a few weeks probably.

As in Beograd the doctors and medical nurses were the Russians, but the helping personnel—service and attendants—were mostly the women from the city. All I had to do was lie there and accept the ministrations of the doctors and nurses and get well. But I missed Colonel Sokolov. There was no one to talk to, no one to confide in. There was little to do but think. Day and night, all waking moments I argued, pointing out to myself all good reasons why I should leave the army as soon as the war was over. Russia—my homeland—yes, but Stalin and his Communists had spoiled it for me. I wanted none of them.

My memory sent a fast series of pictures through my mind and as usual I reviewed everything in my childhood—my school days, the dreadful days in Siberia, the war experiences. I compared all of that life with the life I found in countries just across the border from my own Russia. I couldn't believe it. I didn't want to believe people had a better and happier life than we had in Russia. My stubborn mind wanted to refuse, but there it was all before me. Everything was better, even the Yugoslav nurses in this hospital didn't seem to be living in fear, in spite of the war. Once again I strengthened my resolve never to go home.

Then my memory drew from all the reading I had done from Russian, French and American authors. I had read the first two with serious thought, but the American authors I read with tongue in cheek, thinking Mark Twain and Jack London and the others had a great imagination. Nothing could be as good as they painted it, so I gave them no more thought. Why would anyone write such deceptive stories to fool people!

The doctors and nurses were very attentive; one Yugoslav nurse in particular seemed to come to my bedside more often than was necessary. But I had other things to think about. I wasn't interested in nurses. Besides, I was Russian and afraid we were not too well liked in Yugoslavia even though we had driven out the hated Germans. We were a different people and really we were "occupying" as well as liberating their country. There had been a few street fights and brawls and even though the offenders were picked up and punished, I imagined I saw disapproval on the faces of a few. I felt I should keep to myself and talk to no one.

I lay in my bed, thinking, thinking, but could come to no conclusion as to where to go to spend my life. I seemed to be looking for a moral solution in a world of complete confusion.

Russia, my mother Russia, had let me down, enslaving and murdering millions so that the new rulers could usurp the place of the Czar. They had made of themselves a new royalty, a new aristocracy with all the privileges of the former Czarist rule by enslaving the people far more than the Czar ever did.

I couldn't sleep and didn't want to eat. One day the doctor asked, "What's wrong, young man? What's bothering you? You should be up and out of here, but you're not improving. You're going backward!"

I knew then that others noted my condition and that worried me more than ever. I was afraid I might talk aloud in my fitful sleep. It was at this time that my intellectual independence was born. It dawned on me that a human being had certain rights which other humans had no right to stifle or trample on. I wanted freedom in thought and opportunity. I concluded that I would wait here until I regained my health; go back to my regiment; and, if I lived, I'd leave the army when the war was over. I'd make my way to a new life, a better life for Mother and me in a new land somewhere, somehow.

But now that I had come to a definite decision I wanted to talk with Colonel Sokolov once more. I needed his advice as there were so many technical problems in connection with my future. He was the only person who could answer my many questions and I knew I could trust him. I felt that I had to talk with him about my next great step. I simply had to do it, to unload my heart—full of doubts, hope and pains.

I wrote asking if he was well enough to come to see me, enclosing money for expenses, knowing he lived on a very small pension.

XXIX

A couple of terrible weeks passed as I waited for Colonel Sokolov, looking toward the door every time anyone came in. This mortal torture undermined my health each day until at last: "Lieutenant Sazanov! You have a visitor," announced my nurse and I saw him standing beside her at the door.

After the usual greeting he asked me with a worried look on his face, "What has happened to you, Sergei? You are looking much worse now than you did in Beograd! What is the problem, Son?"

"Let's go into the yard. I'll ask the nurse to help me to the wheelchair. I want to talk to you alone."

"Certainly, we'll go outside."

After we were seated on a bench in what had once been a schoolyard, I looked around to make certain no one was near.

"Well?" he asked as he waited for my words. But I didn't know how to begin, excited and confused as I was.

At last I said very quietly, "I have decided not to return to Russia."

He waited a little while and answered just as quietly, "This doesn't surprise me. I knew it all the time."

"You knew it? How? I never mentioned it."

"Well, it wasn't too hard to know what was in your heart after your questions, comments and general behavior, but, boy, have you thought this thing over with a cool head?"

"Yes, Sir, I have. I think of nothing else, day and night. I will never return to Russia, no matter what happens."

"You know this is a very dangerous undertaking. If they catch you, you will be shot immediately, without mercy. I don't want to dissuade you, but you know the war will soon be over and you can count yourself lucky that you got through it so far with your life; but now you're going into new danger, into a new war, for you alone, and it is a big question whether you will be so lucky again."

"Yes, Sir, I've considered all these things, but I can't go back. I simply refuse to go back. I'll stay here in Europe or somewhere else. I can't tell you all my reasons, but they are very serious ones."

"I'm sure you've had some bad experiences in your life, Son, but what about your mother? Did you think about her? What will she say to this decision of yours?"

"Oh, yes, I've thought about my dear mother a thousand times. Fortunately, there is my brother, Aleksey. He will take care of Mother until I get settled and I feel very strongly that Mother would agree with me in this matter. I know her feelings."

"I see, Sergei, your mind is made up so I'll promise you any help I can give, _if_ the King returns to Yugoslavia or if there will be some kind of democratic regime. We can't know today what the future will be for Yugoslavia. We can only hope for the best but no one can tell.

"Now, at the present time, I am nobody and none of the Russian imigrants know what will become of us in the future. We expect the Russian army will leave as soon as the war is over, which could be any day now. I have a couple of Yugoslav friends in Beograd, very trustworthy men, and they will help me to help you. Just tell me when. You can stay in their homes until the Russian army leaves. You will be safer with them than with me, as of course, I am known as a Russian."

"I thank you for your offer of help, Sir, and I know how dangerous it could be for you and your friends, but I'm not sure about my plans. I don't know where I'll be. I know I must get well and out of this hospital first. Maybe the best thing for me will be to go somewhere overseas, far away from Russia, I don't know . . . "

We continued our conversation on this theme for some time until he said, "Well, Sergei, it is time for me to go. I hope we'll meet again soon. Please be careful. You are standing on the brink of the hardest test you have ever had, and you'll need all the courage and strength you can muster. Once again I wish you luck and success in your plans. I will pray for you, my dear Son." He finished with tears in his eyes.

I returned to my room with a lighter heart than I had had in years. My attitude and my whole being were brighter. When the nurse came in she said, "This is the first time I've ever seen you smile! You must feel better!"

"Yes, I do!" and to myself, "Careful, man. Careful. Don't give yourself away."

XXX

The doctor noticed a marked improvement when he visited me the next week. He told me to go out and walk in the garden, no more wheelchair. I obeyed him and this lovely nurse came and walked a few steps with me. She wasn't really a medical nurse. She and her sister worked at the hospital, helping the personnel in the kitchen and serving meals. After they lost their father, the Russian hospital was the only place they could earn some money to live. She tried to teach me Yugoslavian, and it was really a pleasure to have such a beautiful teacher. Her name was Lisa. Both of us were amazed how fast I learned this language.

She was a pretty girl with golden blonde hair and blue eyes, but she was not for me. I could not become seriously interested in girls until I got settled. I only had one object in mind and the only person I could allow to have a part in it was my mother, Momotchka, my dear Momotchka. I could still hear her voice saying over and over, there at the railway station in Siberia, "I'll never see you again."

Well, if I lived, Mother would see me again and in a far better land.

One day Lisa invited me to her home for dinner. Of course I gladly accepted her invitation. My roommates looked at me with envy and kidded me about my excitement and nervousness. However, all of them tried to help me with my preparations as best they could. A Lieutenant loaned me his new high boots, another officer gave me his shoulder belt, somebody from the next room brought even a pair of gloves. They accompanied me to the door and wished me good luck.

Lisa lived with her mother and two sisters. Her only brother, Josep, was in the Hungarian army and had been captured by the Russians.

The father disappeared one day. Officers from Yugoslav Partisan Army came to the door and asked him to go with them "for a little investigation." The family never saw him again. He was a man of sixty years, a musician, who never did anything against anyone, but in that time many innocent Hungarians disappeared leaving no trace. They were accused of "Collaboration With The Occupants" and were done away with, without trial.

Lisa's family lived in a pretty little house which was surrounded by its own plot of ground with a vegetable garden. Flowers were growing under the trees. They were originally Hungarians, but as this part of Hungary had been turned over to Yugoslavia in 1918, they were considered Yugoslavians. They spoke the language as readily as they spoke Hungarian.

I was in doubt as to how I might be received by the family, being a Russian officer. Even though we had driven the Germans out and were looked on as Liberators, we still had a rather bad reputation for many reasons. Some of our soldiers and even officers committed violence and crime toward the civilian population. Several cases of robbery, murder and rape had happened in Subotica and other places. True, these men were arrested and immediately shot by the Russian Military Police, but even such drastic measures didn't stop the soldiers from violence. It was useless explaining to them that Yugoslavia was our ally and not the enemy. The atrocities committed by Germans on Russian land were used, by our soldiers, as the reason and excuse for their own misdeeds. All they knew were the words of hate and vengeance implanted in their minds by the propaganda machine. "Avenge our fatherland! Avenge our wives, sisters, daughters! Kill the enemy!"—these were the slogans heard by our soldiers every day during the long war time. And now we had the consequences.

These unpleasant matters were on my mind as I approached Lisa's house. I was prepared to defend our people in every possible way. However, my fears about Lisa's family's negative feelings toward the Russians proved to be groundless. They welcomed me and were the kindest people I had ever met. Nothing was mentioned in connection with the behavior of our army. The only remark on this was said by Lisa's mother, when we spoke about the Germans and their responsibility for the beginning of this war. She said: "One cannot judge a whole nation by the deeds committed by individuals." She probably knew it troubled me and tried to help me in some way.

The dinner was great. Lisa's uncle, a cheerful old man, told us funny stories about his soldier's life during World War I. As I talked with them, I noticed they seemed to warm up to me and little by little I gained their confidence. I was very happy in this comfortable home, the first I had been in since Mother and I were snatched out of civilization.

I was invited to Lisa's home several times and every time I went I spent the most enjoyable moments in my life.

XXXI

In April, 1945, restored to health, I was supposed to return to my regiment in Vienna. According to my documents I should reach headquarters within seven days. There was plenty of time, more than I would need for the trip, and it occurred to me that I might visit Colonel Sokolov in Beograd. I could spend some time with him and still make it to Vienna on schedule. I knew it would be a dangerous trip because I was supposed to be going in the opposite direction. The main danger was, of course, the Russian Military Police. Their patrols would probably be somewhere on the road to Beograd. In spite of this, I decided to try it. It was very important to me to talk with the Colonel once more about my plans for escape. There were so many questions to ask and decisions to make. If it was impossible to get through, I would simply turn back.

I traveled easily to a town called Novi-Sad on a train crowded with civilians. There was no sign of Russian patrols; but in Novi-Sad the train stopped and everyone got out, including the Beograd passengers. After asking a few questions, I learned that the bridge across the Danube had been demolished and the only way across the river was by ferry boat. I suspected the ferry boat would be a very good spot for the patrol to be stationed.

Very carefully I chose a position from where, unseen, I could watch the boats and the passengers coming and going. I didn't see a single Russian soldier traveling across the river, and it struck me as a little strange. However, it wasn't a route that Russians ought to travel. The front was far away from here. This could be the reason why I didn't see any Russian soldiers here. No soldiers —no patrols, I concluded. I decided to try the ferry.

I walked with others onto the boat, trying to stay in the middle of the crowd. Everybody was aboard, but the boat still didn't move. "Come on. Start the boat. Come on," I kept saying to myself, wondering what we were waiting for. Looking to the shore I saw the reason for the delay. There were three Russian Military Police walking rapidly toward the boat.

I understood their tactics then, but it was too late; they had been hidden in a small building used as a station house and had been watching from the window. Very smart indeed! I produced my documents, showing my goal, Vienna. Politely, they asked me to go with them to the Commandant for questioning and they returned the documents to me. They escorted me to the building where the police were located; but as it was already evening, it seemed to me none of the officers on duty wished to hear my case. One of them, a big fat major, came out from an office, glanced at me and said to the soldiers: "Put him down."

I was placed in a cellar where I found two imprisoned Russian soldiers. They told me that the police executed by shooting every soldier or officer they arrested if they were suspected as deserters. I knew very well what one could expect in a case such as mine: death, certainly. The soldiers were frightened and feared for their lives.

"We hadn't been trying to desert," they told me. "We just fell behind our regiment, but the police won't believe us. We will be transferred to a jail in the morning and executed."

It wasn't difficult to persuade them to try to escape with me. We had nothing to lose. We investigated the cellar, walls, window, and door. At last we decided to try to remove the door. Before trying anything, we knew we had to wait until the jailer went away. He was walking outside in the yard. We waited a couple of hours, but he was still there, walking in front of the door. We knew we had to get to work. Time was getting short and all we had to use as a tool to loosen the screws on the door was the lid of my watch. We decided to work a minute at a time when the guard was farthest away from the door on his march, taking turns listening for his footsteps.

We carried on this difficult task for about two hours; our fingers were bleeding, our tool was broken, and we had loosened only three screws. By this time each of us should have loosened three screws instead of only one each. We were ready to give up when, suddenly, by the light of a yard lamp which was shining through our one small window, I noticed, on the cap of one of the men, a star! The red star of Communism! That star, the symbol of Communism, would save us from Communism! Each one of us had a star on his cap. We broke off the sharp points of the star and found they made very good tools. We finished our work in ten minutes.

But what to do now? Move the door off and attack the jailer? We decided to wait a little while; surely he'd have to have a few minutes off after walking all night. The time wore on slowly. Every minute was precious and I could feel the dawn approaching.

Suddenly we heard no more footsteps outside. We quickly took out the screws and opened the door. The courtyard was empty so we stepped out carefully and closed the door, but found we must go through the main building to get to the street. The big front door was closed and locked and we knew that there, outside on the street, were two soldiers on guard. We could hear them talking. The only way was through the corridor where there were offices on both sides. We slunk into the corridor and turning the door handles of each office found a door unlocked which had windows to the outside. In a few seconds we opened a window on a quiet, empty street. We jumped out, shook hands without a word, and each went his own way.

I hurried along the deserted streets toward the main road to Subotica. My plan to visit Colonel Sokolov was a very bad one, I had to admit. It was just plain luck that I managed to escape that cellar and death.

I waited some time on the road hoping a car would come along. About dawn I was picked up by a Russian Military Navy car going to Subotica. We arrived there in the morning, but, of course, I couldn't go to my hospital because they knew that I was somewhere on my way to Vienna. Only Lisa knew that I intended to go to Beograd to visit a friend, and I wanted to see her once more before leaving for the front. I was very happy that I could see her once again, if only for a short time. "Beware, Sergei," I said to myself, "you are thinking too much and too often about this girl and you are too happy that you will see her again. These are very dangerous signs and it is a poorly chosen time for sentimental feelings. She is very beautiful but how can you think or hope that she ... you stupid!" I will tell her farewell and go to the station right away, I decided, feeling very strong as I stood at her door.

"Oh, Sergei, It's you!" she cried, opening the door. "Come in, come in!"

"Well," I began bravely, "I really haven't too much time. I just came to say goodbye."

"Oh, no, you must stay and have dinner with us! My mother will insist! You must stay!" She looked at me with those big blue eyes and I simply couldn't say no.

Of course I did stay for dinner with Lisa and her family—I stayed all day and it was dark outside before I remembered that I must be on my way. She went to the railroad station with me. Parting with her was very difficult because I didn't know whether I could escape or whether I would be returned to Russia. I didn't know when I would see her again, if ever.

Lisa knew nothing about my plans so the only thing I could say to her was, "I will return, I promise." And I wanted to return, very much, although I was uncertain about our feelings toward each other. Just as my train gave a warning bell, I asked Lisa if she had a photograph of herself. By "chance" she had one in her purse, a very beautiful one. I looked at it, and my train started to move. I squeezed her hand and jumped on the step. For a long way I could see her as she waved to me. My mother had done the same thing a few years before, far away in Siberia, but Lisa didn't say, as my mother had, "I will never see you again."

I traveled to Vienna the usual way, by Russian Military trucks going in that direction. I stopped in Budapest for a while to see the city and visit Lisa's cousin, Rudy. I had a letter from Lisa's family with me so I could look him up if I had time. My reception was rather cool; but after he read the letter, I was very welcome. He offered me his home to stay the night, but I told him that I had to leave at once. He accompanied me to the street, and, shaking my hand, said, "If you have any problems here in Hungary, by all means, call on me. I will be glad to help you."

XXXII

I arrived in Vienna on the evening of the day before I was due to report. I walked around the city for a while and then decided to go to bed. Sleep, however, was impossible. Many different thoughts went through my mind but Lisa, always Lisa, was foremost. I wondered what was happening to me. Was I falling in love with this girl, **really**? Is this really love? But she? Does she love me, too? Maybe she is only acting the way any girl would act toward a young man. She gave me her picture, but probably only as a parting gift.

The only thing I knew for sure was that when the war was over and I had managed to escape, my goal would be Lisa's town, Lisa's home, and Lisa. I would tell her that I wasn't going to return to Russia; that I would stay in Yugoslavia until the Russians went home; that I would wait for that great moment in Beograd, hiding with friends of Colonel Sokolov. And with those thoughts I fell asleep.

The next day was May 7, 1945. I was standing on the street with a group of Russian soldiers waiting for the truck which would take me to my regiment. Suddenly someone yelled, "The war is over! Germany has capitulated!"

Immediately there was wild confusion—people yelling with glee, jumping around and dancing in the streets. In the first moments of this wonderful news I was as excited as anyone, but in a few minutes I remembered my plan. This was a very good chance to disappear. I need not return to my regiment, just not show up there at all. I hadn't seen anyone from my regiment while waiting for the truck, and I felt sure that in all this confusion I could get away. So, I started to walk toward the center of the city, thinking as I walked, "This is the best time for me to make my escape. Yes, this is the best time. The army will consider me a 'missing person,' the facts being that I had left the hospital but never arrived at my headquarters. I hoped they would assume I had been killed by some enemy, German or Hungarian, on the route to Vienna—those things happened many times in enemy territory. And Colonel Sokolov could inform my mother that I was alive.

I wanted to leave Vienna at once but here was another problem. How could I go **from** the front, with my papers directing me **to** the front? Here was the Novi-Sad situation all over again.

XXXIII

After wandering around the town for a few hours, wondering what to do, I noticed I was standing near a hospital, where wounded soldiers were being loaded into cars. I got into a conversation with one of the drivers and discovered that wounded men were being transferred to the main hospital in Budapest. The next caravan would go this evening. I decided that one of these cars would have to deliver me to freedom. That evening I returned and hid in an adjoining house, where I could see the courtyard of the hospital. There I waited until the loading of the patients began. Then from my pack I took out a large bandage and wrapped it around my head as if I were wounded. I watched the attendants bring the patients from the building, group by group. There were some who could walk but needed a little assistance. Some had arms in slings. Others, like myself, wore head bandages. When the attendants went inside for the next group I crossed the yard, climbed in one of the cars, and sat beside other wounded men. No one paid any attention to me as each man was occupied with his own pain and misery. When the cars were loaded to capacity, we set off and once again I began to hope.

Arriving at the hospital in Budapest, I got out with the others and went into the first men's washroom I could find. There I quickly took off the bandage and walked out to the street.

I hurried to Rudy's house. Thanks to Lisa I had a place here where I could go and a man whom I could trust.

Rudy wasn't too surprised when he saw me at his door. I told him openly that I would like to go back to Subotica, but I didn't know how I could manage it without being caught by Russian patrols. Rudy didn't ask me many questions. All he told me was: "Give me a little time, Sergei. I will go out and look around and see what can be done. Don't worry. We will find some way out."

He returned late in the evening, very tired, but with good news.

"You can't escape in your uniform, Sergei. There are Russian police on every road and in every railway station in Budapest. Only Russian Military trucks are on the roads."

"It's beginning to look pretty bad for me, isn't it?"

"No, not altogether. I think you can make it on the railway. There's a train going to Subotica tonight, about midnight. The station is packed with people waiting for that train, mostly Yugoslavians, ex-war prisoners and forced laborers, going home from Germany. I think you can get on this train, but forget your uniform."

"How are these men dressed?" I asked.

"They're wearing everything you could imagine, even German uniforms."

"In that case I think I should wear German military trousers and boots. Do you think you could find that for me?"

"Sure, just give me a little time."

He went out again. When he returned, he handed me a package, saying, "See how these fit you."

I stood before a mirror dressed in a misfit of high German military boots, trousers, civilian shirt, and jacket; all a little too large. I scarcely recognized myself. I took off the jacket and shirt and put on my own. With my pistol, in its holster, there I stood again: A Russian Lieutenant in full uniform. Trousers? In the Russian army we had many soldiers who wore German trousers and boots. After this test, I very carefully put my uniform on top of my pack where I could find it immediately in case I needed it.

Rudy went to the station with me and showed me the train. As we waited there we watched Russian policemen identifying Russian soldiers. None of the policemen even looked at me, but I still felt uneasy as I expected a heavy hand on my arm at any moment. I had a strange feeling that I still had on my military shoulder straps. I touched my shoulders a few times automatically to assure myself that they were not there.

There was no problem during the trip, but that didn't stop me from worrying. Russian police walked through the train, periodically, but seemed to be interested only in finding Russian soldiers. At the border between Hungary and Yugoslavia, the Russians left the train and Yugoslav soldiers took over. I didn't like this very much, especially when I saw them begin checking the passengers, stopping at every seat and looking over the papers of everybody. Slowly I rose and stepped into the washroom where I quickly changed into my military shirt, then walked into the next car. There, to my dismay, I saw other Yugoslav soldiers checking passengers from the other end of the train. As I passed them in the car aisle, they saluted and greeted me in broken Russian. I gave them the friendly greeting, **Zdravstvujte**, * and smiled at them.

I left the train at the small station on the edge of the city of Subotica, rather than go on to the main station. In the first convenient spot—it was a niche between two buildings—I quickly changed again into civilian clothes. Then I hurried toward Lisa's home. It had been a very short time since I had left her. What would she say? What would she do when she sees me in these clumsy "civvies?" Wouldn't it be better to change back into my uniform just for this important occasion? Surely it would be better and I must do it. Lisa knows me as a Russian officer in a fine uniform and not in this conglomeration. I said to myself, "All right, let me find some place to change." Just then I saw two Russian soldiers walking across the street and all thoughts of changing clothes left my mind at once.

"Well," again to myself, "at least I will know what she likes about me, me or the uniform."

I arrived at her home and knocked. When she opened the door she stared at me from head to feet. "You, Sergei, you!" she cried and lifted her arms to me, and—there she was in my arms.

I kissed her and said, "I love you!"

"I love you too, Sergei," she whispered.

"In these rags?" I asked, looking at my clothes. "You don't even ask me why?"

"Oh, yes, I like your clothes very, very much—much better than your uniform. And I don't ask why. These clothes tell me that you have returned to me forever!"

---

*How do you do.

XXXIV

It was the happiest day of my life. I stayed with Lisa the whole day talking, laughing, dancing and planning wonderful things for our future. Lisa's mother invited a few of their relatives and everyone was happy.

I told them that I was going to live in Beograd with friends of Colonel Sokolov until the Russian army returned to their homeland.

"It is a large city and I can disappear there. I will be just another man among many thousands and not noticed."

Lisa accepted my explanation, but not too willingly. I could see that she had some other ideas in her little head.

"No, Sergei, don't go now. Stay a few more days in Subotica," she begged.

I couldn't see why not, so it was arranged that I should stay in a small hotel, just a few blocks down the street. The "few days" became two whole weeks. I couldn't understand how the time could fly by so fast. In the meantime, I wrote to Colonel Sokolov and the answer came, "Everything is okay. We are waiting for you." However, Lisa was still against my leaving.

"My brother, Josep, is expected home very soon. He's been away for over a year and I want you to meet him before you leave for Beograd. It is very important to me that he meet you."

I must admit I was glad to have some reason to postpone my leaving Subotica. It was so wonderful to be here with Lisa, to see her and speak with her every day.

A few days later Lisa's mother invited me to dinner. Josep was expected. There was to be a great celebration and the finest dinner the land could provide. After some hesitation, I decided to wear my uniform for the dinner in order to make the best impression on Josep.

I had certain misgivings about meeting Lisa's brother as he probably had reason to dislike the Russians. He had been drafted into the Hungarian army, as the Yugoslav territory where they lived was annexed to Hungary during World War II. He had been taken as a war prisoner by the Russians and now had been released. (The Hungarian army fought with Germany against the Russians.) Further, we Russians were here in his country, his homeland. I didn't know what to expect, but I knew I'd have to meet him sooner or later.

As my contribution to the dinner I bought a bottle of "Tokai" —the finest wine I could find, and I managed to "procure" some coffee and sugar to take to Lisa's mother.

We were gathered in the living room where a cozy fire glowed. As we sat comfortably waiting for Josep to arrive, I could see the table in the dining room set with a lace tablecloth and beautiful dishes. Judging from the aroma emanating from the kitchen, I knew a good dinner was waiting.

Suddenly the door opened and in strode Josep, a tall, handsome man with black hair and eyes, just the opposite of his blonde sisters.

The mother and sisters flew to welcome the warrior home with tears and kisses and cries of, "Josep, at last! We thought you'd never get here! How fine you're looking!" This they said in spite of his worn and ragged appearance. Yet, his dignified bearing belied the shabbiness of his war prisoner's uniform. I could see his tunic had been made for a much smaller man and the old German boots he wore told me he'd been in the thickest of the fighting just as I had. He looked as the true soldier home from war—worn and tired.

Lisa introduced me. He took me in at a glance. After hesitating only a moment, he greeted me and shook my hand. His manner was polite, but cold. He might not love the Russians, but he had to be careful. The Russians were masters of this country and the people were afraid of them.

He endured my presence in his home, but I felt that he would have preferred to show me the door. After again measuring me up and down, the whole six feet of me, he turned and stalked out of the room. Everyone was silent. A moment later the mother followed him and from the other side of the door we heard Josep say, "Mother, what does this mean? How friendly is Lisa with this man?"

"Hush, Josep! Lisa wants to marry him. We all like him. He's a well-mannered, gentle young man!"

"Mother, I don't want to hear his good points recited. How

long has this been going on?" he snapped.

"Josep, Son, don't be so angry. Lisa has known him for five or six months and has been bringing him here for the last couple of months, at my invitation."

"At your invitation?" he stormed. "You mean to tell me you've invited this man to our home? Didn't you think of what I might say on this matter?"

"Yes, Son, yes ... "

"Mother, please don't 'Yes' me. This can't go on. We can't allow Lisa to take up with a Russian. He has nothing to offer her and my sisters must marry well. Oh, yes, I know the Russians are our friends. They drove the Germans out and all that. He may be a fine fellow, but we can't encourage this. I might as well break it up right now!"

He turned to the room. His face was dark with anger, though he seemed to be making a great effort to control himself. Lisa stood close to me, gripping my hand and trembling in fright. She started to speak, but I silenced her. Stepping forward, I looked Josep straight in the eye.

"I heard what you said to your mother. It is not necessary to tell me to leave. I'll go and I only hope you'll come to know I care for your sister in spite of the circumstances."

With that I bowed to the mother and squeezed Lisa's hand and closed the door quietly as I went out. I had scarcely reached the gate when Lisa, bareheaded and pulling her coat on as she ran, caught up with me.

"Sergei, I'm going with you," she cried as she caught my hand.

"No, Lisa, no," I said gently as I pulled away from her. "You can't do this, I can't take you. It's impossible. Josep is right, I have nothing to offer you!"

"Sergei, the war is over. We'll get along!"

"No, Lisa, it's impossible. Yes, the war is over, but not for me! I have to hide for awhile. You know that."

"Never mind. We'll live through it and we'll be together!"

"Lisa, darling, you don't understand. When I get settled and safe, I'll come back for you!"

"No, I'm going with you now!"

"Lisa, I truly wish it could be. I love you with all my heart, but it can't be!"

I tried to break away from her but she caught my coat sleeve and nearly tore it off.

"There, you've said it, 'I love you with all my heart,' I love you, too, and I'm going with you no matter what you say," she cried, tears streaming down her face as she pounded on my chest with her fists. "You're mine and I'm yours forever!"

I grabbed her wrists and held them tight. "Lisa, I must tell you again. You don't know what you're saying. You forget we can't be married. I would be arrested if I went to the authorities for a marriage license, and I'll never take you out of your mother's house without marriage!"

"Oh, Sergei, of course not. Of course not. We can be married!"

"No, we can't. I've just told you!"

"But we can. I know a way! I know a way!"

"Lisa, say no more. You are beside yourself because of Josep's actions. You must calm down now and I'm taking you back in the house. Promise to meet me tomorrow at our usual coffee shop and we'll talk it over. Promise?"

At once we were in each other's arms, I was smoothing her pale hair and kissing her wet eyelashes. In the darkness as we clung together, knowing, without a word, that however the way, we would be together always.

I could hardly sleep that night. Different ideas came to my mind, but all of them were rather impractical. If I were only free, I thought, sitting sadly on my bed, but like this, there is no hope at all.

The next day, I felt very dejected, sitting in the coffee shop waiting for Lisa. It was most painful to think we had to part from one another. True, it was my first intention to go to Beograd immediately after arriving here, but so many wonderful things happened since that time. I know I had to go to Beograd shortly anyway, but it would be an entirely different situation. I would know my Lisa was waiting for me. Yet even now, someone was trying to separate us by force. If I go away, Josep will do everything in order to destroy our love. If I stay, he will forbid Lisa to see me at all. Many unpleasant things could happen to all of us. Obviously, Josep doesn't like us Russians, and who knows what he would do in his rage. Maybe it would be better to go away and not provoke him. Then, without realizing, I said aloud, "But how can I explain all this to Lisa?"

Suddenly I heard her say, "You don't have to tell me anything." I lifted my head and there she was, standing by my table.

"Oh, sorry, Lisa, I didn't see you," I said, rising.

"I see you have a lot to think about, darling," she continued as I seated her. "But first let me tell you some good news, Sergei, and please don't look at me so sadly, or I will start to cry right here at the table," she said, trying to cheer me up.

The news was really good. It was possible that her mother would help us against Josep. "All we need now is just a little time and I promise you Josep will change his mind." Lisa explained to me her "military plan!"

"Mother knows how to handle my big brother. Please, Sergei, be patient." She gave me a kiss and ran away.

XXXV

A few days passed. We met in the coffee shop regularly, and Lisa informed me about her progress with "the stubborn elephant," as she called her brother.

Although I was disappointed and angry, I could find it in my heart to feel sorry for Josep, confronted as he was with two women, who, it seemed, had decided to win at any price. We laughed many times as Lisa told me about some of the comical situations in her home.

"We are very lucky that my mother is on our side at last. You know she wasn't very happy about you at first. I'm sure you understand."

"Yes, I do understand; she is a mother and wants the very best for her daughter. That is only natural."

"But now," continued Lisa, "when she sees how unhappy I am with Josep objecting so seriously to our plan, she is more than ever on our side."

"Well, then, I'd say the battle is half won, wouldn't you?"

"It's hard to say. There's very little conversation in the house and a sad mood seems to have taken over, but yesterday it was rather funny... " and Lisa started to laugh and continued, "After a silent and cheerless dinner, Josep hit the table with his fist and yelled, 'It's enough! Have you all lost your power of speech, or what? All I hear is yes or no around here—and who cooked this dinner anyway? I can't eat it. It's pure salt!!!"

"Mother answered, 'Lisa cooked today while I was busy, but don't be so angry, Josep.'

"With that he jumped up and gave me a furious look and ran out, slamming the door. We laughed at his show of temper. Then about an hour later my aunt came to see us and said Josep had stopped at her house on his way downtown.

"My aunt said he was in a terrible rage and explained he

didn't want his sister to marry a man who had nothing tangible to offer. She told him that we were certainly in love, and what could be more important than love?

"'Love has nothing to do with it,' he yelled.

"Well, then my aunt told him how ashamed she was of him for acting this way, and many other 'nice things' about his actions. I think he'll remember it for a long time," Lisa said with a smile.

"After my aunt left," she continued, "Mother and I laughed and cried, but mostly laughed. A little later Josep came in and went straight to his room. We heard him slamming things around and mumbling to himself: 'Heartless man! Cruel character! Inhuman creature!' and the other 'nice things' my aunt had said to him. Mother and I smothered our laughter as we listened and Mother whispered, 'I give him two or three days more!' "

Lisa and I laughed but I couldn't be sure Josep would relent. He was a very stubborn man and he felt he was on the right side.

Two or three days later when Lisa and I met at our usual coffee house, Lisa had a big smile on her face. As we sat waiting for our coffee she leaned over and whispered, "My Mother was right—we won! Josep sends you his invitation for dinner tonight!"

In a sort of daze I presented myself at Lisa's home that evening. Josep met me at the door, hand extended, and invited me in. After a few general remarks, we settled down to talk.

"You can't blame me for being particular about the man my sister marries," he began.

"No, I can't," I admitted.

"Since my father's disappearance—and death, we presume—I am responsible for the family. You, of course, understand my objection to the marriage; however, since our last meeting, Lisa has told me a great deal about you and I see my mother approves. But before making a decision, please tell me more about yourself and your plans for the future."

I told him briefly about my life in Russia and when I said I had decided never to return there, I noticed he was interested.

"I expect to go to Beograd to hide with friends until the Russian army leave Yugoslavia."

He gave me a long, searching look, obviously thinking over what I had said, then remarked, "Well, they should be leaving very soon now, and the sooner the better. But what is your plan after they leave? I mean how do you intend to make a living?"

"You probably remember I told you about my friend, the ex-Russian officer who later became a Colonel in the Yugoslav army.

He is a man of influence and has assured me that he would find some office job for me to start with. I was always good at mathematics while in school, and I think with work and study I can become a fair accountant. With the support and protection of Colonel Sokolov, I know I can earn enough to support us."

At that point the mother came in and announced dinner.

XXXVI

"Now for a celebration!" Josep shouted. "The war is over, my sister is to be married, and I have a brother! Drinks for everyone!" He grabbed his mother and danced her around the room and before I knew it someone put a record on and we were all dancing. More and more wine was poured and I danced the Russian "Kazachok" and everyone was happy. We sat down to a beautiful table and a wonderful family dinner.

"Now for the serious side," Josep said as we finished eating and sat drinking coffee or sipping wine. "I now have a brother; and, Mother, you have two sons."

"Yes," she smiled, "he is one of us. I have two sons."

Lisa's eyes shone at me from across the table, but she said nothing.

"Your plan to go to Beograd is a good one," continued Josep, "however, I have a better idea. My uncle—you know him, Sergei—has a room with a separate entry and from the back yard you could easily go in and out without being noticed by anybody. Something just for you. It is close to our house and I believe Lisa may like that better than your going to Beograd. What do you think of it, sister?" He turned to Lisa with a twinkle in his eyes.

Lisa smiled happily. Naturally, I accepted Josep's offer, gladly. It was a wonderful chance to be with Lisa. All my reasons for living in Beograd disappeared.

"Do you need some clothes, or something else?" asked Josep.

"Oh no, thank you. I have civilian clothes and can get more. I still have plenty of the money from officer's salary for the past several months when I was in the hospital. Perhaps you've noticed I've been wearing a Yugoslavian haircut ever since I've been here. I am sure that I will not be noticed. It'll only be a short time because I think the Russians are so sick of war they'll get away as fast as they can—it's just a matter of a few days."

"Yes, I agree. When the Russians start to move, they MOVE! Didn't we see them drive the Germans out of here?"

"Josep, will you have more coffee?" the mother asked.

"No, Mother, but I'll have some wine. Lisa, how about another glass all around? Wine, Sergei?"

"No, I'll stick to coffee, thank you," I answered. "But I'm still not sure about my staying here instead of going to Beograd."

"The Russians will go away, but until they do, you're to stay right here, in Subotica. It's settled, I'm older than you, see?" He grinned across the table at his mother.

"Josep' s word is law—you are to stay, Son."

Lisa smiled her approval with her eyes full of tears, and lifted her glass to me, so it seemed it was to be that way.

The next day I moved into my new home, and a new period of my life had begun. All I had to do was wait, wait patiently, and be careful. So I did. Most of the time I was in my room taking the opportunity of making a real study of the Yugoslav and Hungarian language. The uncle, as everyone called him, and his wife were the most pleasant people I ever met. They did everything possible to make my life more enjoyable. I visited Lisa and her family frequently, but I also had to be careful not to show myself too often on the streets. Approaching Lisa's house, from across the street, I would watch a front window for a signal which we had agreed upon. If visitors were in the house, the mother, or whoever was at home, would take the bouquet of flowers away from the window. If there were no flowers, I would keep on walking. As soon as I saw the bouquet I knew I could go in.

"I've always liked flowers," I told Lisa one day, "but now I love them, all kinds of them. They'll always have a very special meaning for me."

Lisa laughed. "I'm so glad we thought of flowers for our signal of safety for you."

"I only wish flowers could be in the window all the time," I answered.

"I do, too, but the neighbors have been so friendly lately. Mother and I are making my wedding dress and we can't let them see that. This is strictly a family affair until the right time comes."

So, they're making Lisa's wedding dress! Bless my Lisa! Well, she had nothing on me. I had bought our wedding rings without telling her at some risk in going downtown where I might be noticed, and now I had them safely in my pocket.

The time of waiting for the Russian Army to leave Yugoslavia stretched into weeks and I began to feel I was a burden to the family, but Josep reassured me over and over again. "No more talk of that. Now I have a brother and I'm going to enjoy him, and boss him around, too!" And, indeed, we spent many pleasant evenings playing cards and chess and discussing Capitalism versus Communism and guessing the future of Europe and its devastated condition.

Lisa and I often took walks in the evening under the cover of darkness. That was our only time to be alone. I thought no one other than the family knew I was living in the uncle's house, but one evening Lisa said something that made me think I was wrong.

"My friend Barbara—I've known her all my life—told me there is a Russian soldier living in her mother's house, and she invited you to come over to see him. She says he's lonely for someone to speak Russian with and maybe you'd like company too."

Seeing my surprised look, she continued, "I don't think we need be too alarmed. I suppose there are several of them hiding here, though I've never seen any. Perhaps you'd better go see him. His name is Pavel."

I didn't like this too much. If Barbara knew I was in the uncle's home, how many others knew it? However, curiosity got the better of me and I went to see Pavel. He proved to be a Russian Sergeant who, even in civilian clothes, saluted me in the usual military manner.

After a couple of visits with him, he invited me to go with him to another home where I could meet several of our soldiers and officers. I didn't like this either, but again curiosity won out and I went.

XXXVII

I found my Russian friends in a large, fine house behind a high fence. It spelled danger to me, but there I was. The host was an ex-Russian Captain, a military doctor, quite young, who introduced himself as "Captain Kolja" and I answered in a like manner, "Lieutenant Sergei." One by one other guests introduced themselves: "Sergeant Vanja," "Lieutenant Sasha," "Private Volodja," and so on. They all wore civilian clothes. No one gave his last name. There were about twelve of them, all young men who preferred not to return to Russia. It was very interesting to speak with them, as all of us had the same problem. The main topic was, of course, "When will the Russians leave Yugoslavia?" and "What will be the new regime in Yugoslavia?"

I noticed that nearly all of these young men planned to marry a Yugoslav girl. In spite of the danger of being shot they preferred not to return to Russia. I wondered what would happen to our army if the soldiers would be permitted to stay in Europe if they wished?

During the conversation I noticed no one asked what regiment I had been in or the name of my home town. That seemed a very smart rule, but these parties, in my opinion, were not a good idea. Even though we were all in good humor, full of plans for the future, I still felt uneasy.

I learned how they were living now, here in Subotica. Some of them, mostly officers, still had money. The Captain, a professional physician, was already taking patients, but how he managed to do it was a mystery to me. I thought it was a great risk. Perhaps he was relying on the general confusion. Two of the soldiers were working on the farms of their future in-laws. Others were dealing in black market, unable to find any other way to make a living. One of them, becoming very friendly, offered me a glass of wine and asked if I needed money. If I did, he said he could help me earn some.

"You know," he confided as we sat on the couch together, sipping our wine, "I have a brother here who is still in the army, but he is going to stay in Yugoslavia after everything is cleared up. He is a driver of a truck and his unit is in a town not far from here. He drives to Budapest bringing back military supplies and several of us go with him. We are merchants now," he laughed.

"What do you sell, and how?"

"We buy lard and oil here and sell it in Budapest. You know this part of the country was not hit as hard as some other parts and the peasants around here seem to have plenty to sell. We make a good profit."

"But how about the border and the Russian patrols on the roads in Hungary?" I asked, amazed at his story. I wondered if the wine had gone to his head.

"Don't worry. Everything is working out. Somewhere before the border I put on my brother's military overcoat and cap. With his gun in my hands, I act as a guard over the rest of us who sit there in the truck with their hands behind them as if they were tied. At the border gates we must stop, of course. But you know that Yugoslavs have no right to question the Russians who are in a uniform. However, the border guards are after civilians they see in our truck. 'Who are these men?' the guard asks me. 'They are Germans! Damn Fascists!' I answer, and give him a big sheet of paper written in Russian. It is really only an old Russian bill of lading form, where we have written a few German names. The guard looks at this important document' then begins to count names and the men in the truck. 'Everything is in order! You may go! Lift the gates!' he orders. Funny, isn't it?" He laughed again, and so did I.

"But you don't always travel the same road, do you?" I asked him.

"Of course not. Each time we take a different road to the border. When we get into Hungary we stay off the main roads, where the Russian patrols are. And how about you?" he asked me again. "If you need money ... "

I thanked him and said I still had a little money. His invitation didn't interest me. I didn't escape from the army to play some smuggler games. If I could have only known then what the future held for me, I wouldn't have been so sure of myself.

I visited this home several times even though I felt uneasy every time I entered the door, but my enforced idleness seemed to take the edge off the danger. It was my only opportunity to talk with Russians and perhaps I might learn something advantageous. At least that is how I argued with myself. Each time we met there were a few more men, and I learned some of them were Communists.

Usually I visited this home with Sergeant Pavel as we lived near each other. I advised him how to dress and conduct himself so that he wouldn't be suspected of being Russian, but he didn't listen to me. He wore a suit which was decidedly Russian in style. The coat was much shorter than the Yugoslav or European style, and the coat shoulders were straight and short, the Yugoslav were a little longer, and the Russian trousers were much wider than the Yugoslavian. Even his hair was different—cut high on the back of his head while the Yugoslavians wore theirs longer. Since he spoke neither Yugoslavian or Hungarian, I told him he should take all precautions.

I felt it wasn't too clever of any of us to go to these meetings, pleasant as they were. We had formed a regular club where we drank and played cards. I had heard the Russian Military Police and the Yugoslavian soldiers were practicing razias* and were capturing Russian deserters. When I voiced this fear at the club, most of them just laughed at me. "The Russians will leave very soon, but we will stay here! Stop worrying, Sergei!" they said to me. Only a few of them agreed with me. However, nothing was done. We continued our meetings as before.

---

*Searches

XXXVIII

The weeks and months passed without any change. To our great satisfaction the Russian Army started to move their units from Yugoslavia, but at the same time another danger appeared for us refugees from Communistic Russia. Yugoslav's Communistic Party grabbed all the ruling power in the country. The main reason for the Russian troops' leaving was that they were sure the Yugoslav Communistic Party would maintain its pro-Russian regime. Our one big hope that Yugoslavia would have some kind of Democratic government was shattered. Colonel Sokolov's letters from Belgrade were also very concerned about the whole situation. He, himself, was in trouble as a King's colonel, let alone his anti-communistic escape from Russia. He was very sorry, but he had to advise me to come to Belgrade only if it was absolutely necessary. He thought that any place in Yugoslavia would be now less dangerous for me than Belgrade.

Our club was completely confused. Nobody knew what to do. Most of us agreed that the only way was to escape from Yugoslavia, but where? To the West? The allies were there—American, English and French troops. They represented countries with Democratic, non-communistic governments. But the allies, according to a war agreement between them and Russia, had to turn every Russian refugee over to the Russians. This agreement was followed without exception, unfortunately for us.

We still met at the doctor's house, but these meetings weren't like the old ones. No laughing, or jokes, or beautiful plans for the future. Silence and worry were the masters now, as though death was among us.

One day Pavel and I were on our way to visit our friends when suddenly in the street we saw four Yugoslav soldiers coming directly toward us. "What now?" Pavel asked, nervously.

"Calm down, Pavel," I answered. "First, I'm going to try

something. If it doesn't work—run to the left. But wait for my signal."

"All right," he said.

As the soldiers approached us they, of course, noticed at once that Pavel wasn't Yugoslav. They stopped us and asked for our ID cards.

"Odmah, drugovi,"* I answered in Yugoslav and began to search my pockets for my card, which of course I didn't have. Instead, I wanted to offer them money. I heard that it worked many times. But Pavel shoved his way through the soldiers swearing in Russian, not even waiting for my signal. He probably hoped the soldiers would back down, but two of them ran after him with guns in their hands. The other two kept their guns on me, waiting for my ID card. As the soldiers caught up with Pavel, he suddenly pulled out his pistol. A soldier fired and Pavel fell down. At the sound of the shot the two soldiers with me looked in that direction. It was only a second, but I had already started to run down the street. I rushed to the nearest house, followed by gun fire. I glanced back and saw Pavel sitting on the ground. He was probably wounded in the leg. Three soldiers raced toward me, shooting and yelling. I ran across a garden where people were eating their breakfast, jumped over a fence and found myself in a cemetery. I ran across to the other side and came out slowly, just in the nick of time to catch a street car. I knew then that I must leave the uncle's home immediately because if I were caught there, the whole family would be implicated and the penalty would be death for me and a long imprisonment for the rest of them.

I went to my room quickly and was getting some things together, only the barest necessities, when Josep came in. I told him what had happened and that I must leave right away, but I didn't know where to go.

"Well," answered Josep thoughtfully, "you get ready while I go out to see some friends and make some arrangements for you. We'll see later what we can do about it."

We both knew that the house could be entered and searched without a warrant or order of any kind. It happened every day. Men were arrested, taken away and never heard from again.

Josep had already gone out, when it hit me—heavens, Kolja, Sasha and the others! "Josep, come back. Josep, please come

---

*Right away, Comrade.

back!" He hurried back to my room and I continued, "I need your help. Find somebody, a friend you can trust, and send him to Kolja's house now, right away, to tell Kolja what happened with Pavel. Please, Josep, hurry now, please ... " and I almost pushed him out. My God, I hope it isn't too late to save them.

Then I started to clean my room. I worked quickly, destroying everything that looked as if it might have belonged to a Russian. I burned all papers that had any of my handwriting on them. Now my uniform—I held it in my hands, reluctant to put it into the fire. I could ask the uncle to hide it somewhere. No, I couldn't. If the police found it in his home, they could accuse him of murdering a Russian officer. Heaving a sigh, I put the uniform into the fire. I must destroy it. Watching as the fire in the stove slowly consumed it, I felt that I was burning a part of my life.

By the time Josep returned I was ready to go. "Well?" I asked him impatiently, "did you find someone to inform Kolja?"

"Let's go outside first, Sergei," he answered, not looking at me, "or it will be too late for you, too."

"What do you mean, too late?" I questioned him as we hurried along the street. "It is impossible. It's been only two hours since they caught Pavel!"

"Sorry, Sergei, but all your friends who went to Kolja's today were arrested in his house. Oh, it wasn't because of Pavel. The Russian Military Police surrounded the house early in the morning and waited until the last of the Russians entered the house. Then they went in. The people on Kolja's street saw the whole operation. You, Sergei, may thank our Yugoslav soldiers for stopping you on the street. Otherwise ... " Josep didn't finish the sentence.

Lisa told me later that shortly after I left, the police came and searched both houses completely, without saying what they were looking for.

Josep took me to the home of friends, a very nice home and pleasant people who made me welcome, but I couldn't sleep that night. Pavel, Dr. Kolja, Sasha and all the other Russian friends of mine were in my thoughts. I feared they would all be killed.

I recalled Dr. Kolja, a very fine, intelligent man who surely would have had a good future in Russia as a doctor, but chose not to return. He risked his life in the war but lived through it, only to die now. He was a Communist, as he mentioned once. I asked him one day why he decided never to return to Russia.

"Well, it's a long story, my friend, a long story, the same

as every one of us here could tell, including you---" he pointed at me, "but I will tell only one thing to you. You, of course, know about it, but it was a horrible experience for me, as a military doctor. You have probably guessed it. It was the famous order of our great leader, Stalin, about the soldiers who lost their guns. You know the punishment for losing your gun—execution by shooting. But we, the medical personnel, had another order. We were forbidden to give any medical aid or to accept in the hospital any wounded soldier if he did not have his rifle with him. They were refused admittance and told to go back and find the rifle; only then could we take care of them. Many, many of them, seriously wounded, never came back. It was so cruel, so horrible, to refuse to help them and I'll never forget it, never. I simply cannot go back and serve again our beloved Stalin and his inhuman assistants."

Poor Kolja—now he would never serve anyone again.

XXXIX

A whole week I stayed alone in my room. No one from Lisa's family visited me during that time, because they could have been under police surveillance. I had plenty of time to think over and over my badly changed situation. It was clear to me that I couldn't stay in Subotica any more. The police knew about me and my connections with Lisa's family. My arrest would destroy Lisa and her whole family. I had to go, no question about it. The question was where to go and how to go.

My previous plan to go to Beograd wasn't a good one any more, not only because of Colonel Sokolov's letters, but also because of the new ID cards given to the Yugoslav people by Tito's regime. Everybody had to carry his ID card with him at all times or he would be arrested and imprisoned until his identity had been established. To travel without an ID card would be pure suicide for me.

Besides, why should I go to Beograd? What could I expect now, here in Communistic Yugoslavia? Wasn't it the same thing that I left in Russia? It was the same monster I was trying to escape from who was still here breathing down my neck.

The only place I could go was Hungary, whose border lay 12 kilometers from Subotica. I learned that the border wasn't guarded too strictly by that time. What I liked most about Hungary was the Democratic regime established in that country. In spite of the Russian Army, who occupied Hungary, there was a manyparty system. A non-communistic party, a so-called "Small Proprietor's Party" was the most favored by the Hungarian people. True, the Russian Army was there, but did I have another or better choice?

By the end of the week, Lisa's family came to visit me, one by one. First was Josep, then Lisa and her mother. Our hosts made coffee and we sat around the table. Josep told me about the bad situation in the town—arrests, raids, search parties and a constant check of identification on the streets. I knew that all this was a normal practice of every Communistic regime in order to frighten the people and strangle their resistance right in the beginning.

I told them briefly about my decision to go to Hungary. They all knew the danger we were in, so they agreed that I must go.

"I'm going with you!" Lisa announced, looking straight at me without a flicker in her eyes.

"No, Lisa, you can't," came from everyone at the table.

"Lisa, you don't understand. I'm making an escape. I can't take a train. I have no passport, no ID card. I have nothing."

"Never mind. I'm going with you."

I looked across the table at Lisa's mother who sat staring with grief-stricken eyes, but saying nothing.

"Mother, dear," I begged, "won't you tell her it's impossible? Please talk to her. You know I can't take her."

The mother shook her head. "I don't know what to say. She knows I don't want her to go, but she's twenty years old, and I don't know what to say to her."

"Well, I know what to say," Josep broke in. "Lisa, this is madness. You're not going. So that ends it."

"Oh, yes, I'm going."

"Lisa," I interrupted, "you don't know what you're saying. I'll have to travel on foot and in the darkness across the border."

"Never mind. I can see in the dark and I can walk, too. I have good shoes," and she held up a foot.

"Lisa, it's dangerous enough for me alone, but listen to me. I want you to go with me. You'll never know how much, but it is taking you to a living hell if we are caught. You have no idea how women prisoners are treated. No, you can't go."

"We won't be caught!" succinctly, stubbornly.

"No, you won't be caught," yelled Josep, "because you're not going—I'll tie you up here if I have to!" and he rose from his chair and made a threatening move toward Lisa.

"Mother, if Josep tries to tie me up, I'll kill myself. If I'm going to die, it will be with Sergei. Life here without Sergei would be worse than any death," and she walked around the table and leaned over her mother. "Mama, surely you must know how I feel." Her mother began to cry, with great heaving sobs.

"Lisa," I started to argue, "we're not married and no priest can marry us without a license, which you know we can't get, and I can't take you out of your mother's house without her blessing and the blessing of your church," I said, thinking that would stop her.

"We'll be married, and we will leave together. Do you have our rings?"

"Yes, of course I do," I replied. I looked at Josep, who stood there, his face a study in thunderclouds, seeming to be gathering his forces for one more try. But Lisa, the whole five feet of her, marched right up to the giant Josep and standing in front of him said quietly,

"Josep, no matter what you say, I'm leaving with Sergei."

And to me, "When will we go, Sergei?"

"I think tomorrow night, Lisa," I answered, defeated completely. "Can you be ready?"

"Of course I can. Mama, may we go home now? I have much work to do," and they left the house.

"Well," said Josep resignedly, "I guess by this time you know women," and he looked at the ceiling, and sighed. "But let me give you some directions to the home of my friend. He lives in a small village very close to the border. Just mention my name and he'll help you."

He drew a map on a piece of paper and explained to me in detail how to reach the village. It was pretty clear to me as I knew the town well and its surroundings.

XL

Carrying two small bags and an extra one with Lisa's wedding dress, we left the house by the back door. Lisa guided my steps straight to the church. Josep and the mother followed us.

The streets were mostly lighted, and Lisa walked ahead. I was behind her at a fair distance. In case she was stopped for an identification check, I would have time to hide or go to another street. But nobody was on the streets, and no one stopped us. It was like God himself guarded us on our way to His house.

When we entered the quiet empty place, lit only by a few candles, Lisa asked me to wait a moment by the door and disappeared into a small side door. I wondered where she went. Had she a secret pact with the priest to marry us without a license? But I knew that was impossible.

She didn't keep me waiting long. The door opened. My darling Lisa; dressed in white with a long train and a crowned veil, stepped out smiling. She was a vision that left me breathless. Together we walked down the long aisle to the altar and there we knelt and promised to love and honor each other for the rest of our lives. We exchanged rings. Then we recited the Lord's Prayer together. "God will consider us married," she whispered. When I kissed her, indeed I knew He would.

Josep and Mother, with tears in their eyes congratulated us and wished us Godspeed.

Quickly Lisa changed into her dark dress. Carrying her precious wedding dress in a bag she put her arm through mine and smiled. We ventured out into the midnight quiet of the town streets, together, arm in arm, completely forgetting about police, danger, and about the whole world. We walked northward out of town, on our way to the Hungarian border.

Not a word was spoken. I prayed silently to God to show me the way to take care of this girl who loved me so much that she dared to face exile, or even worse.

After leaving the city we came to a forest, and following Josep's directions, we found his friend without any trouble, about two o'clock in the morning. He willingly got out of bed and accompanied us to a spot near the Hungarian border. He showed us a path which would take us directly to the road which marked the border line.

"Just wait by the road," he cautioned us, "and listen for the footsteps of the guard. He passes every hour all night. Watch for your chance and cross over. One on the other side, walk to the fourth house on the right, where my uncle lives. Call him Antal-Bachi* and tell him you are from Yugoslavia. He and my aunt will take you in."

"How about the patrols on the Hungarian side?" I asked.

"There are no patrols on that side. Just be sure you get across before daylight!"

We said farewell to the man and taking our luggage started to walk very carefully. I walked first, breaking trail, and Lisa close behind me, carrying her beloved dress in its case. We hadn't gone twenty feet when it started to rain. We knew we had no time to stop under a tree to wait for the shower to pass; maybe it wouldn't anyway, as this was the autumn when severe rains could be expected. We trudged along and as the rain came down heavier—almost a cloudburst—the path was impossible to follow. We got down on our hands and knees in order to feel the way. The shrubbery was dripping, really drenching us, making us much wetter than if we had been walking instead of crawling.

At last we came to a huge tree and I saw the road which must be the border. The pouring rain was the only sound. We waited behind this tree—it was a big, old oak, and listened, not daring to even whisper, waiting—it seemed forever—waiting for the guard to pass.

While standing in the shadow of the tree I remembered the many experiences I had lived through during the war, hiding, running, hiding. Colonel Sokolov was right, the war was over, but not for me. That moment was a preview of what lay ahead of us. How many such crossings I would be making and how much more dangerous they would be with Lisa to take care of? What kind of life awaited us?

But in spite of the terrible danger and the new responsibility

---

*Uncle Antal

of caring for Lisa—the sweet loveliness of Lisa so near me—I tasted, for a fleeting moment a deep sense of happiness, exquisite happiness.

At last I heard footsteps and Lisa gripped my hand at the same moment, showing me that she had the same sense of hearing and smelling danger as I. Mine was trained into me while in the war, but Lisa's must have been born in her along with that great heart full of love which she expressed in all she did and said. My Lisa. Who and what am I, I thought, that she should love me enough to share my uncertain life?

We waited. The rain began to slow down and finally it stopped completely. At last we heard the guard walking toward us, and past us, in his slow measured tread. After he was well out of hearing, we crossed over. We were in Hungary and safe at last.

It was nearly dawn when we finally entered the sleeping village. Only a couple of dogs barked at us. We found the fourth house on the right and knocked on the window as instructed.

"Ki az?"*

"Mink vagyunk, Antal-Bachi, Yugoslavia-bol,"** I whispered.

The man opened the door and welcomed us. His wife gave us a glass of brandy which was gratefully received, wet and cold as we were, and after a change of clothes, a wonderful meal was set before us. Lisa and I called it our wedding breakfast.

Later I asked Uncle Antal how we could travel to Budapest since we did not have Hungarian ID cards. He laughed and said, "Here in Hungary, nobody will ask for your identifications, so you can travel by train without any trouble. But, in any case, you may tell them the truth. You are refugees from Yugoslavia and the police will give you your ID cards without any question. Thousands of our people are arriving here every day from Yugoslavia, Rumania or Czechoslovakia."

He drove us to the railway station where we caught a train to Budapest. There we went to Lisa's cousin Rudy's home.

Everything happened exactly as Uncle Antal had said it would. At the police station we were asked to fill out a form and sign it. Nothing else. In Yugoslavia you had to show your birth certificate, but here you could write anything you wished. I wrote:

---

*Who is it?

**We are from Yugoslavia, Uncle Antal.

Name: Shandor Kovach
Nationality: Hungarian
Born: In Temishwar, Rumania
Married. Wife: Lisa Kovach

Lisa whispered to me, "Why did you write Temishwar?"

"You never know what may happen to us in the future. It is better if nobody knows where we are from," I answered. We stood in line and waited our turn. At the window a girl smiled at us and handed us our ID cards.

A new man, Shandor Kovach, was born. How long will he live?

XLI

Our new life in Hungary had begun. My Hungarian was fairly good. While living with Lisa's family I heard and spoke nothing else. We rented a little apartment with a kitchen and I began to look for some kind of work—an almost impossible task, as all the factories were ruined and closed. I discovered people were happy to earn just enough to buy food. The city people were taking their clothes, shoes, bed linen and anything of value to the villages to exchange for food. The peasants had food, but didn't want money. Due to inflation the pengo* fell in value every day. There was a great deal of confusion and every man had to find his way in any manner he could.

Lisa found a job again in a hospital kitchen, but I wandered around for days trying to find something to do. Just any kind of a job would do. In the course of looking around, I made quite a few acquaintances. One day I remarked casually that I could speak Russian.

"Can you really?"

"Yes, sure. My grandmother was a Russian and she taught me. For a time we lived in Czechoslovakia and the language is very much like Russian."

"All right, boy, come with me. I can get you a very good job with a local merchant here. He is in need of a man such as you."

He introduced me to a man he called Aladar. "This is my friend and he speaks Russian. I guarantee him."

Aladar explained the work. "Here in Budapest there is a great lack of food and our peasants in the villages have food for sale, but they can't get rid of it on account of lack of transportation. The State hasn't enough cars, trains, trucks or gasoline. But there are many Russian military trucks, and you, speaking Russian, could perhaps find some Russian driver with a truck, who,

---

*Hungarian money

for good money, could go with us to the villages and bring back the food. I will pay you well. In a couple of trips you will make enough to live well for a month. In this inflation, I can't say exactly what the amount will be, but it will be enough."

"But," I asked, "how will you pay for the food? I've heard the peasants don't want the pengo."

"Dollars, my young friend, dollars. Everyone wants dollars. Best money in the world. But that is my business. Your job is to find a Russian driver with a truck, then go with me and act as my interpreter. You know, I don't want to go alone with a Russian soldier. It will be safer with you along. What do you say? Accept my offer?"

I started to think. This business wasn't new to me. It was the same thing I heard about from my Russian friends while in Yugoslavia. In my rambling around looking for work since coming to Budapest, I heard more than once that the Russians were making good money in illegal transportation. I knew the risk was great. It would be dangerous for me to go among the Russians, I might be discovered. Something unforeseen might happen. I reasoned with myself, but the need for money won out.

"Well?" Aladar asked, anxious to get the deal closed.

"All right, but let me see what I can do about a truck and driver."

"Yes, that is the main thing right now, after secrecy." He smiled and winked. "But when we have the truck, everything will run smoothly. You'll see."

When I got home Lisa was cooking dinner, a very skimpy dinner, I thought. It made me think of the life in Leningrad when we had to search the markets for barely enough to eat. In Subotica there had been plenty. That particular valley was very rich and productive. We could buy anything we wanted, although all parts of Yugoslavia were not so fortunate.

I watched Lisa as she put the food on the table. I wanted to apologize to her for the poor quality as I felt I was a poor provider.

"Well, now, Lisa," I remarked in a gay tone of voice, "we are about to end these poor rations. Your husband has a job and things will be better from now on. You can quit your job at the hospital very soon. How does that strike you?"

Lisa stood halfway between the stove and table, the coffee pot in her hand. "Why, that's too good to be true! What happened?" She was all smiles.

I told her all about the proposition, and her smiles faded.

She was positively against it.

"Oh, what are you thinking? Do you want to destroy us? Please, darling, I beg you, don't do this thing. It is too risky, and I don't want to lose you."

"Now, don't worry about losing me," I tried to reassure her. "I know my way around and this Aladar is a smart businessman. He knows his people and his city. He was born here in Budapest and he has been a merchant for years. And I know the Russians. I'll get along. Come on, now. Let's eat."

Lisa sat down at the table but hardly touched her plate. She looked at me. "Darling, be patient just a little longer. We'll get along on what I make until you find something better—and safer. Just wait and you'll see!"

"All right, since you feel so strongly against it, I won't take the job. I don't want to worry you. I'll look for something else." She kissed me and we went on with our meal.

XLII

The next day, however, I went over to the Russian barracks and warehouses, just to look around, I told myself. There was a cafe where Russians came to drink one or two Palinka* every day. I came in and stood by the bar listening to the conversation. After a while I saw a Russian driver who was having a difficult time making the waiter understand his order. I approached them and translated to the waiter what the soldier wanted to eat. Of course the soldier was happy that at last there was somebody who understood him and he invited me to his table. I spoke very broken Russian, being careful not to pronounce words too clearly.

During our conversation I learned all I needed to know. He was the right man. I knew he would be in this bar the next day about five o'clock and I was casually there too, of course. We greeted each other as though we were old friends and sat down at a table and talked about everything in general. Time passed and I impatiently sat there, wondering how to start talking about the thing that was weighing on my mind when suddenly he asked, "You do need transportation, don't you?"

I was astonished. "Well, yes, but how ... ?"

"It's nothing, my friend. I've done this many times. Just tell me when, where and how far it is from here and I'll give you my price. And --" he leaned closer, "I must tell my captain first. He shares in the profit after supplying the truck and gas. I'm a soldier and can't go without orders. He gives the order for some 'official duty' and then I may drive."

"So that's how it's done?"

"Yes, I see you get the picture. You understand, everyone must live—you, me and the captain."

---

*Hungarian brandy

The next day all arrangements were made and a few days later Aladar and I, with our Russian driver, went on our first trip to a village. There were a couple of Russian military patrols stationed on the road. They checked the documents of our driver and, finding all in order, we were allowed to go on. The Russians were not permitted to have civilians in their trucks, but we had several bottles of palinka for such 'cases' and it proved to be a very good 'permit' for Aladar and me. When a soldier opened the truck door, we simply pushed a bottle in his hands; he put it in his pocket and let us go.

In this way we transported food to Budapest for about eight months. It was usually lard, flour, pork or beef and other foods as we could find them. Out still-unknown captain gave us his truck generally three times a month and often Aladar had to supply the gas as the captain didn't want to be suspected of giving out too much of it. He worked with not only us; there were other traders and he had several trucks in his command.

Of course I didn't tell Lisa immediately about the work. I told her I had some temporary work until I could find something better, but after the first trip I told her the truth and gave her the money. She was greatly agitated and begged me to stop this dangerous business.

"Shandor (she called me by that name since coming to Hungary), I can't take this money. We can't live this way! I won't know when I'll hear that you've been caught and executed. In reality, you may be executed without my ever hearing about it. You know how they operate!" and she burst out crying.

"Lisa, my dear, you are taking the wrong attitude. There is no danger at all," I lied. "All I do is interpret Aladar's instructions to the driver. We have a Russian truck and driver, and papers signed by a Russian captain which let us through all inspection stations. Just don't you worry any more, I'm perfectly safe."

I succeeded in calming her fears to a certain extent and promised to stop immediately if there appeared to be any danger.

We soon moved to a better apartment and I persuaded Lisa to quit her work at the hospital. Her earnings for her hard work were so small compared with mine, that it was senseless to carry on with it. We were very happy in this time of our lives. We were young and in love. We didn't want to think of the future when the present was so wonderful. These were our real honeymoon days—joyful, though dangerous. I learned to take risks during the war, so to live in peril was normal for me.

However, every trip became more and more dangerous. These illegal transportation trucks were seen on the roads so often that the Russian Military Police established many new special patrols along the roads. In order to evade them, we traveled only at night and on small country roads where no patrols were stationed.

One day Aladar said, "We'll have to stop. These trips are beginning to be very risky now. Also, there seems to be enough food in the city, enough anyway so that there's no more profit for us."

I gave this news to the driver. "Just wait. I'll see you later," he remarked and disappeared.

XLIII

A few days later as Lisa and I sat finishing our evening meal, I heard a knock on the door. There was my driver standing in the darkness. I asked him in; but before he entered, he asked if we had guests. Being assured we were alone he came in and said quietly, "My captain, who has been signing our orders, is here and would like to talk with you."

"Bring him in, by all means," I said, but my heart began to pound. What can this mean? This captain whom I have never met, what can he be wanting with me?

The captain came in. Captain Tolja Lehov, in full Russian uniform. He was a man about thirty-five, a usual Russian officer. There was nothing extraordinary about his appearance, but I was surprised at his business acumen when he began to talk.

Lisa quickly brought fresh cups and we invited them to have coffee with us. The captain came right to the point. "In a few days I am going to Vienna. As you know, they are having the same food shortage that we had here in Budapest until recently. If you want to go, I'll take you along and we'll look the situation over. If we find any business, I'll give you a truck for transportation, as I did before. However, there may not be quite so much profit because of the longer haul. Otherwise, just the same. Agree?"

"But there is the border between Austria and Hungary. How about that?" I asked.

"That'll be my end of the business," he answered. "Remember I'll be in this too and I'll take care of you at the border. Don't worry on that score."

He looked at Lisa with a smile trying to allay her obvious nervousness and dissatisfaction with the deal, and said, "I'll bring your husband back alive and in good health, so please don't worry."

Aladar consented to go with us and in a few days we were on the main road from Budapest to Vienna. This time our captain used a different system. The truck was loaded with various equipment for the hospitals. Under this equipment there was a large box, labeled "medicaments" and there, inside that box Aladar and I were hidden. The box was large enough for us to lie down. I felt as though I were in a coffin. The lid was left open during the trip until we approached a guard station—our captain knew very well where they were—then the driver covered the case and placed packages on top of our 'house.

Arriving in Vienna, we went to the home of a friend of Aladar which we later called our headquarters. The captain and Aladar went immediately to investigate the business situation. I had other things on my mind, which was the main reason I consented to go on this journey. I wanted to know, first hand, whether the Americans were still extraditing escaped Russians out of Austria back to their own home country.

This was my second visit to Vienna and I noticed great changes. The streets were full of people; the tram cars were operating; and the stores were open. People seemed to be living normally.

There were four sectors in the city: American, English, French and U.S.S.R. Our headquarters—Aladar's friend's home—was in the French section. After a short walk, I found myself in the American sector. There were no patrols. Everyone could go anywhere he wanted so I had no trouble getting there. It was so easy, good Heavens! I could just as well be living here in this freedom with my Lisa. But what would it be worth if there was danger of being sent back to Russia?

I walked around the American district for some time, watching with envy the United States soldiers and officers, well dressed and well fed, with apparently no worries. Then I went to the building where the Common Command of Alliance was located and saw U. S. jeeps driving in and out of the courtyard. In one jeep were four officers, American, English, French and Russian. They seemed to be looking the town over. I looked at them, sitting there all together in such unity, and I thought, "No, it is impossible; it can't be so! I can't believe it! But what can it do for me now? Nothing!"

I walked over to the Russian Commandature headquarters to try to find something, anything, that might perhaps throw some light on my chances of escaping extradition. Watching nearby, I saw Russian soldiers go in and out of that big, high building with two Russian soldiers standing at the entrance, as guards.

I didn't learn anything of importance, but later, Aladar who spoke German very well, told me a great deal of the political situation and about life in Vienna and in all of Austria and Germany. He mentioned that Russians who were placed in the camps in the American part of Germany and Austria, ex-prisoners of war and forced workers, were sent back to Russia.

Later he remarked in a more cheerful (to my ears) tone, "I think there will be some business here. I can sell oil, the cooking and eating kind, and lard, at a good profit. We'll talk with the captain."

That evening the captain—we referred to him as Tolja—arrived at our headquarters and after a short conversation we reached an agreement. Tolja asked more for his share and for gasoline but that was understandable. There was more expense in transportation as there was a much greater distance to travel.

We returned to Budapest the same way we came—in our 'house' with the freight—military uniforms, hospital supplies—loaded around the house and on top of it.

Aladar had the merchandise ready for our trip to Vienna. The car was loaded, as usual, with military supplies. Our merchandise, lard and oil, was put in barrels resembling gasoline barrels and labeled 'gasoline.' I saw the captain write on his Transportation Order Book, "Ten barrels gasoline." Aladar sold this merchandise very easily.

XLIV

These trips had continued for about a month when one evening as Lisa and I were finishing supper, we heard a knock at the door, giving me, as usual, a nervous start. It was only Captain Tolja calling to tell me there had been a change of time for the next trip.

Tolja seemed to be a very fine fellow, judging from the little I had seen of him, so I invited him in. He had been drinking palinka and was rather talkative.

"Lisa, how about a fresh pot of coffee?" I suggested, thinking it better not to offer strong liquor.

We sat at the table talking, Tolja accepting the coffee politely from Lisa. I think our little home, the table with its white cloth and the presence of a lovely woman, made Tolja homesick, as he began to talk about his home. I was glad he was self-centered enough not to ask me about my life before the war. If he had I was ready for him. My story was well fixed in my mind.

"You know, I was a teacher in a small town in Russia—a nobody with nothing. Now that the war is over, I'll go home and be a teacher in a small town again, with a small salary—a nobody with nothing, just the same as before."

I said nothing but listened closely, while Lisa busied herself pouring more coffee and offering cake.

"You can't understand, young man and young woman," he continued, "the life we have in Russia. I have a wife and two children and I would like to give them something more than I gave them before; maybe a radio, a gramophone, bicycles for each, and maybe a motor cycle for myself."

I stole a quick glance at Lisa, but she didn't notice as she was listening intently and I wondered what she was thinking. I was concerned about what Tolja might say next; perhaps he was sent here as a spy and was trying to draw me out, so I continued to give my attention to him.

"No, you can't understand it," he continued, "because here in Budapest and in Austria you have everything—good clothes, shoes and everything. And you know I'm not the only Russian in this black market business. No, everyone who can manage to get into it is doing the same thing. We transport lard to Vienna, others take cigarettes from here to Czechoslovakia. By the way, please accept a couple of packs," and he passed them over to me.

"Thank you, but I don't smoke," I answered.

"Take them anyway. Give them to someone," and he paused to light one. "And we bring salt here from Rumania. Everyone who knows how, trades, and the aim is the same—to take something home, back to Russia; if nothing else, several watches. We don't have them in Russia for the general masses, you know. They are too expensive."

"Is that so?" I asked, as though I were filled with wonder.

"You don't believe it, do you? All right, you don't need to, my friend. I only hope you never have conditions here such as we have in Russia."

Heavens, I thought, how fast our people change. How soon we forget all the austere Communist teachings. Just let us get away from our Russia and see with our own eyes what other people have, and we soon forget our conscientious Soviet principles and become like everyone else—just people wanting a better life for ourselves and our children. Is it so shameful, as the Soviets would say, that we turn away from their empty promises and want a few bicycles for our children, a radio in the house, and a wrist watch? "No, by God, it's only human!" I understood what Captain Tolja was thinking and feeling.

Later I asked our driver if Captain Tolja was a Communist.

"Of course," he answered and he looked up from tinkering with the truck's engine, "but he is a very good man. Don't lose faith in him," and went on with his work.

Yes, I thought, everyone must live, soldiers, Communists, even Security Police. Hurry, hurry, hurry, grab everything he can get. There at home awaiting him is misery. Give him dollars, gold, or watches. Why watches? They are small and easy to conceal to carry home and will bring a good price. Yes, watches, watches, watches.

The Russian soldiers collected watches in Beograd, Budapest and all the towns wherever they were sent. Everyone understood the Russian words, "Davai chase."* In Budapest there was a joke;

*Give me a watch.

A Russian soldier went into a watch shop and placed a large alarm clock on the counter and said, "Make me two wrist watches from this, buddy."

One evening Lisa and I were in a theatre listening to the famous Hungarian comedian Latabar Kalman. When another actor asked him what time it was, he pulled up a sleeve where there were several watches. Then he pulled up the other sleeve showing several more watches. Finally he pulled up the leg of his trousers and there were several more on his leg. He glanced at all of them and said, "It is nine-thirty." There was great applause, because everyone knew what and whom Latabar wanted laughed down.

The next day Latabar was sentenced to a month in prison for anti-Russian propaganda.

XLV

Our business trips to Vienna continued during the summer of 1946 to the satisfaction of all parties. But, unexpectedly, something happened which destroyed not only our company but almost cost us our lives.

One evening in Vienna, Aladar and I relaxed in our room waiting for Captain Tolja to pick us up for the drive back to Budapest. It was dark by the time he arrived, cheerful as always.

"Hello, boys! Sorry to be so late but I have a deal for you, if you are interested. A friend of mine has a car he wants to sell and I think it's a bargain. You could sell it in Budapest for a good price. Come on with me to see it!"

A few blocks' walk and we were in the Russian sector where we stopped at a house with a small garage in the rear. We went in the house, where by a light of a gasoline lamp, a Russian officer waited for us. He stepped forward, and then I saw something that I had hoped never to see again. I stared but couldn't believe my eyes; the color on his epaulettes and on his military cap ... N.K.V.D., of course, but ...

This face! This voice! Yes, it was he again. No doubt of it! Lt. Morozov! No, pardon me—it is Captain Morozov now! "Gora s gorog ne vstrechajetsja ... " Once again it was night in Leningrad, my mother lying on the floor near the wall with blood on her face ... then the Ukraine front flashed before my eyes, the penalty battalion, "the glory to die for the Fatherland," and he standing beside me in the trench.

Believe me, I didn't need to try to act and speak in broken Russian, I couldn't find one single Russian word, even to greet him.

Of course he didn't recognize me. Who would think this stranger, this Shandor Kovach, was Lieutenant Sazonov in the trench in Ukraine, or the same boy he snatched out of his home one night five years ago in Leningrad? Control yourself, Shandor, I said to myself, as I felt my blood begin to boil.

Out in the garage, the business was concluded quickly, as the car was very good and a rare buy. In Budapest it would sell for double the money. There was only one problem—how to deliver that car in Budapest without a license; but Morozov already had a solution.

"If you will pay me a little extra, I will drive the car to Budapest for you," he said, "and maybe Tolja will introduce me to some pretty Hungarian girls. Won't you, Tolja?" he laughed.

His proposition to drive the car seemed fair enough and we agreed to it.

Standing there so close to that man looking at the infamous color on his epaulettes, I thought, "Yes, he said it was his own car, but he couldn't know that I knew that in the Russian Army no one had his own car. It was a war trophy' which really belonged to the state and he took it for himself." For this, or much less, he, as a captain of the N.K.V.D. could degrade me and send me to the penalty battalion as he did with others during the war.

Aladar and I walked out of the garage, but Captain Tolja and Captain Morozov stayed inside talking. Some inner warning told me that all was not as it should be; that something evil was brewing—as was usual with Morozov.

"Aladar," I whispered, "you stay out here and talk in a loud voice, talk as if you were two people so they will think you are talking to me." He looked at me, not understanding.

"Hurry. I must hear what they are talking about," I said and left him. I took advantage of the darkness and quickly but quietly approached near enough to the garage to hear them.

"Skazu-fashisti, napali. Pulja v zatilok i vse gotovo... Pridut moi rebjata, otvezut. Nikto ne sprosit—kak, pochemu. Moja rabota, Ja otvechajem. Dengji—popolam. Idet?"*

There was no answer immediately—Captain Tolja was evidently thinking it over, but at last he said in a low voice, "No, buddy, they have their families. Their wives will ask me and later they'll go to the military police, our illegal transportation will be discovered and everything will blow up. It's no go."

---

*I'll say that Fascists assailed me. A shot in the back of the head and all is finished. My men will come and take them away. No one will asky why or who. It is my responsibility. Money fifty-fifty, all right?

But Morozov's lust for murder persisted. "I have friends in the military police, you know. They'll cover it up; the thing will be mislaid until it's forgotten."

"Well...I don't know...it may work," Tolja hesitated, "but it's too much of a risk."

"But, Tolja, don't be foolish," insisted Morozov. "This is an excellent chance. You'll see. Everything will go smoothly and quickly. You know I'm an expert at this kind of job," and he gave a short laugh. "How much money do they have?"

"I think about a thousand dollars between them. But look here, I don't like this ... " Tolja's voice was strained.

"All right, all right," giggled Morozov, "don't worry. I'll do it without your help and it'll be worth the trouble."

"Bud sto budet. ** But how? Where?"

"At once! Now! Why wait?" demanded Morozov. "A bullet in the back of the head and it's all over. I'll send for some of my boys and they'll have the bodies buried in less than an hour. Here and now, I am the law! Let's go!"

"Wait a minute," Tolja stopped him. "Not here, no. Later would be better, somewhere in the forest on the way to Budapest, but I don't want anything to do with it. You'll have to do it yourself; I have no stomach for this."

"All right, you gutless one," Morozov laughed.

Quickly I went back to Aladar and we talked as if I had been there all the time, though I was shaking so I could hardly control myself. A few minutes later I heard the two captains approaching and I heard Tolja say, "Let's go home, boys." We walked over to our headquarters; the streets were dark and there was no one around. Aladar and I managed to walk 'politely' **behind** the two captains. Who knows, I thought, Morozov might lose his patience.

Arriving at our headquarters Morozov produced a bottle of vodka, "To celebrate," he said, "the conclusion of our business." He seemed very contented and sang as he poured the drinks. He tapped my shoulder, "To you and Aladar! To your health!" he toasted with a smile.

Captain Tolja sat quietly, looking into the glass of vodka he held in his hand. He probably had pricks of conscience. I drank with them, laughing and seemingly carefree. The vodka seemed to warm everybody and we unbuttoned our coats and Morozov hung his

---

*What is to be, will be.

pistol belt on the back of his chair.

"Do you know what I think?" asked Morozov. "You two could go with us in my car—your car, now. It will be better than going by truck, in your 'house' again. What do you think, Tolja?" and he turned to him.

"Oh, yes, Morozov is a big wig and he'll get your car through all the Russian patrols without any risk."

Morozov looked at me, waiting. "Of course," I answered, "with pleasure, Captain, thank you. As you say, it will be better than riding in our 'house'."

"Yep, this time you can ride in style with me as your chauffeur," he laughed and satisfied with his joke he toasted us again. "I think we should start about midnight, just after they've changed the road guards."

"Aladar, show them your collection of pictures," I suggested. Aladar got out his pictures of pretty girls in scant clothes.

"Wow!" exclaimed both captains as they looked over the pictures between drinks. I stood between Morozov's chair pretending great interest and pouring the drinks. Then Morozov hauled out some pictures of his own. They didn't hear or see anything. They were so absorbed in the photographs, it was easy to take the bullets from Morozov's pistol.

I stood there thinking, well, maybe this will be some help, but who knows? I should have listened to Lisa; but it was too late to do anything about that now. I put my attention on plans to get out of the deal alive.

After looking over the pictures several times and drinking a couple of bottles of vodka, Morozov decided it was about time to leave.

"Tolja, suppose you go out and tell the truck driver he can start now, he doesn't need to wait for us. Wait, I'll go with you."

Being on the alert every minute, I jumped to the window and opened it a little as the two captains went out. I heard Tolja say, "You can go now, Comrade, I will follow in Captain Morozov's car. The other two have decided to stay here a few days," adding carelessly, "See you later." The truck rolled away.

Morozov laughed, assuring Tolja, "They don't suspect a thing. Vse idet kak maslu."*

They returned and a few minutes later we were ready to go.

"All is going as smooth as oil.

The car was still in the garage so we walked there once more, but still behind our captains. Aladar and I sat in the back seat and we started on our journey—maybe our last. At the border we ducked down on the floor and covered ourselves with a blanket. When the guards looked at Morozov's documents, they saluted and the road was ours.

XLVI

We crossed the Austria-Hungary border and drove on toward Budapest. After a few miles the car slowed down and stopped beside the road. "Oh, boy," I thought, "here it is," and my heart started to pound. "Stupid fool, why didn't you escape when you had a chance, back in Vienna? Or maybe you thought they wouldn't do it? How crazy can you be?" Well, if this was to be the time and the place, I could waste no more time cursing myself. I must act and act quickly. I had no idea what I would do, so I trusted myself that I would know when the right moment came. At least I knew for sure that he couldn't shoot us with his empty pistol.

"What's wrong?" I asked, wondering if this was part of his plan.

"I don't know, but one of the rear wheels isn't acting right," Morozov answered. After looking in the tool compartment he added, "No hoist. Would you fellows give me a hand?"

It was a beautiful Hungarian night with a full moon. We were in a forest with no village near, not even a farm. It was really a very fitting place to meet death.

"We'll have to find a piece of wood, a log or something, to block up the car. Tolja, will you get the other wheel out while I look for a block of some kind? Come on boys, let's see what we can find."

After a few steps Morzov remarked, "Looks like peasants have been cutting firewood. We ought to find something here."

I looked at him. I still couldn't believe he would try to kill us in cold blood. He behaved so naturally, so normally, that it was impossible to imagine he could calmly kill two men in another minute or so. We came to a pile of wood and Morozov was now behind us and said in an almost cheerful voice, "Okay, boys, this is the end of your journey!"

We turned around. He stood a few steps from us with his pistol in his hand and a satisfied smile on his face. So it wasn't to be "a bullet in the back of the head." He intended to have some fun!

"What is this? What do you want?" asked Aladar.

"Money. Give me all your money, both of you, and I'll let you go. Be quick about it!"

We pulled out our money and put it on a tree stump as he directed.

"Can we go now, Tovarish Captain?" pleaded Aladar.

"Yes, of course," he answered as he lifted his pistol and pressed the trigger, once, twice, three times ... nothing! He looked at the pistol surprised and confused, and that was my chance.

I rushed at him, and as he fell, he dropped the pistol. A terrible rage took possession of me. In that second I saw again the blood on my mother's face. "Now you will pay for hitting my mother," I screamed. His pistol was in my hand and I hit him on the head, face, anywhere I could hit. "This is for my mother! My mother, do you hear? And this is for me! For me! And for Russia, for all of Russia," I yelled as I struck and struck and struck.

"Shandor, stop it. You'll kill him. Let him up," Aladar kept yelling, trying to pull me away. Finally I got up and tried to catch my breath.

"You're too late, he's dead," moaned Aladar. "What ... what'll we do now? My God, Shandor, we are going to the dogs! What can we do?"

"Wait a minute. Let me think," I said sharply.

With trembling hands I loaded the pistol with the bullets I still had in my pocket. There was Morozov's military cap on the ground and I put it on my head.

"Aladar, lie down there on the ground near him and act as if you are dead!" I commanded.

"Now what's this crazy idea? What do you think you're doing?" he asked nervously as he looked at the pistol in my hand. I noticed his frightened face and heard the panic in his voice.

"Get down there. He's not the first dead man you ever saw. Believe me, I mean you no harm; I have a plan to save our lives. Do as I tell you!"

"But Shandor, this is crazy ... " objected Aladar.

"Look, Aladar, we're in a tight spot. Morozov was going to kill us, and in a minute his pal may be here with his gun and finish us off. There's no time to lose. Get down there on the ground!"

"Well, this scheme of yours had better be a good one or we're both gone," he answered as he obeyed me.

I fired two shots in the air and imitating Morozov's deep voice

I called as loudly as I could, in the direction of the car, "Tolja, come here!"

I stood behind a bush. Only my head wearing Morozov's red-starred cap could be seen; and six steps away were two bodies on the ground in the shadow of a tree. Tolja passed by me and glanced at the bodies. "So you've done it," he said quietly.

"Yes, but not the way you expected," I answered, standing just behind him. "Don't move!" I pressed the gun to his back and took his pistol from him.

He seemed to have lost his voice;he didn't utter a word. He looked at me, then at Aladar who had gotten to his feet, then at Morozov's body. "I see, he is dead and you are living ... I'm almost relieved, but of course you don't believe me," he said at last.

"No, I don't believe you!"

"What are you going to do with me? Kill me too?" he asked coldly, as he stood there in the moonlight, tall and straight with his shoulders squared. He was a brave man, he didn't ask for mercy.

"You should be killed, Captain, and you know it, and I've a great desire to do it right now."

"You can't get away with it. Not for one day can you get away with it. They'll catch you."

"Catch me? How? Who saw us in the car? You, yourself made sure the patrols saw only two men in the car. You told the truck driver we would stay in Vienna for a few days and for all anyone knows we are still there ... "

"But Shandor, hold on a minute ... "

"Here are only you and Morozov," I continued. "Someone would find your two bodies with pistols and money in your hands—a quarrel and killing over money."

He was silent as he stared at me. Aladar moved closer to me, standing just behind me. Perhaps to give me moral support, but he made no remark.

"It was clear work, wasn't it, Captain? I really don't know why I shouldn't kill you," I said, looking at the pistol.

No one spoke. I was aware only of the silence as I stood there trying to make up my mind what to do.

"All right, Tolja, maybe I'm a fool."

He looked at me as if not believing what he heard. "I swear I didn't want all this, Shandor. You saw I didn't want to be here with him."

"Yes, I know it and I'm hoping there are still some human

feelings in your heart. Let's go now."

"Wait a minute. Him. What about him?" pointing to the dead Morozov.

"Well, Captain, that is really none of my business. Ti xavril kashu ti eje i rashlebyvay."*

He didn't answer and the three of us returned to the car. Tolja opened the trunk compartment and took out a shovel, and returned to the forest without a word. He knew if Morozov's body were found, he would be charged with the murder.

"I still can't believe I'm alive," said Aladar as we waited near the car. "It was a terrible experience."

"Yes, horrible," was all I could answer. I didn't want to talk about it.

"I'm grateful to you for the way you handled the whole thing, and I'm glad you were with me on all our trips. Without you I might have been killed many times, and tonight's affair—I want you to know I appreciate it very much."

"Here, here, cut out the praise. I was desperate. My back was against the wall. I did nothing more than any other man would do who was fighting for his life."

"Well, I never could have done it. This trip is my last, Shandor, and I'm giving you half my profit. Oh, no, no, you take it. You deserve it. Take it and I thank you."

Aladar was very nervous as he paced back and forth while we waited for Tolja to return from his grave digging detail.

"Come on, Shandor. Let's go now without Tolja. Who knows ... these murderers ... Come on, let's go and just leave him here."

"We don't need to worry. I have both pistols. We're in command now."

"Shandor! Shandor!" Suddenly we heard the excited voice of Tolja as he ran toward us. "He's alive! He's not dead! He's half conscious!" Tolja gasped. "What now?"

I hesitated a moment. "Let's take him with us. He deserves to die there in the forest as he planned for us, but we can't leave him."

"What'll we do with him? He'll probably die on our hands. Then we'll be in for it," said Aladar.

"Guess we'll have to take him to a hospital. Come on. Let's

---

*You cooked the goose and now you eat it.

get him and get out of here, fast!" I replied.

We returned to the forest where Morozov lay moaning, half conscious. Tolja took off his shirt and we bandaged the half-dead man's head, then carried him to the car. During the drive back while looking for a hospital, I had time to think, and the full impact of what I had done, hit me. I had deliberately tried to kill a man —I, who had so recently found God. I had great difficulty controlling myself.

In the first town we came to we found a small Hungarian hospital, where Morozov was admitted immediately, but we were asked to answer questions. Of course, expecting this, we had our story ready.

It seemed hours as we waited while they examined Morozov. All three of us were pacing up and down the waiting room, each with his own thoughts. I didn't know what the others were thinking, but I was praying the man would live, I thanked God for my own life and for my darling Lisa, and begged to be cleared of this awful deed. The doctor came back and announced that Morozov would live. He wasn't wounded very seriously. This news was a great relief to me.

When the doctor asked us who the man was and what happened, Captain Tolja took over, dictating, and I interpreting. We gave Morozov's name and rank and said we'd had an automobile accident.

As the doctor started to write his report, I said, "Please, Doctor, make a carbon copy of your report. The Russian officer requests one."

The doctor of course made the copy and I took the paper for myself. This would be 'proof' that Morozov was injured in a car accident. If later Morozov would see the report with the signatures of the doctor, Tolja, Aladar and myself, he would have no choice but to accept it. Tolja added in Russian, "Injured in automobile accident." Tolja asked the doctor to phone him in Budapest and keep him informed of Morozov's progress.

It was still dark outside and we hurried on to Budapest where I handed the two pistols to Tolja, asking him to return Morozov's to him.

"Yes, when I see him, but what I want to know is how you managed to get his gun in the first place."

"That's my secret," I answered, "and I'm sorry our business has ended this way, but Aladar has lost his confidence and I can understand why. Anyway, what do you think, Tolja? Will Morozov accept our statement to the hospital?"

"I think he'll be glad to. Don't worry. When he gets well, he'll go back to Vienna and you can bet he'll never mention this." I hoped Tolja was right.

After a "See you later" we separated and I got home just before daylight. I didn't tell Lisa anything about the night's activity; she was frightened enough as it was. I simply told her the business had come to an end because there was no longer any profit, and she was glad to hear it.

But I couldn't forget that terrible night and knowing Morozov as I did I couldn't believe that he would forget it either without attempting to avenge himself. I was right. He didn't forget.

XLVII

One evening in autumn, just after dinner, there was a knock at the door. When I opened it, and not without caution, there stood Captain Tolja. I hadn't seen him since that night in the forest, though he had sent his regards to me several times through his driver. I couldn't imagine what had brought him to see me. I invited him in and offered him coffee; he thanked me but didn't accept it. He was in a very serious mood and came at once to the point.

"I see you're wondering why I'm here. I'll be brief. You're in danger! It's none of my business, but I learned casually that you're to be arrested very soon. I'm afraid Morozov didn't forgive you." Lisa looked at me with a question in her eyes. "But it is not because of our trips to Vienna and your quarrel with Morozov. He wouldn't dare mention that. This is something else. He has discovered something, but I don't know what. I only know that you'll be arrested. Maybe they have a good reason. Perhaps you will know."

He looked at me, waiting for my reaction, but I managed to control my feelings.

"I don't know how to thank you, Tolja..." I tried to say something, but he interrupted me.

"Don't thank me, Shandor. Let's just say it is better for my health if you are free ... Arrested you might speak about our business. It could be very unpleasant for me. And now, goodbye, and good luck to both of you."

He started to go but stopped at the door. "You know, there's a way out through the rear of that wrecked building next door. I'll go that way instead of your front door. I advise you to go the same way," and he disappeared.

Lisa and I stood for a short moment, speechless. It had happened so suddenly and unexpectedly. "But, Lisa, we must hurry.

We must go. In just a few minutes it could be too late," I whispered.

Quickly and silently we put the most important things in two small bags and five minutes later we slunk out the back door and through the wrecked building to the street. Now, hurrying, without running—we didn't want to be seen running—we went forward, forward, until Lisa stopped at a corner. "Where, Shandor, where are we going?"

"Yes, really where?" I answered and we stood looking at each other for a long moment. "Austria? The United States sector in Vienna?" I suggested.

"Oh, no, not the United States sector. You know the Americans will send you back to Russia."

That brought me up with a start. Of course I knew. What could I be thinking?

"But, Lisa, we must go somewhere. We can't stay here in Hungary. Oh, my God, is there no safe place in this whole world?" I asked desperately, but there was no answer. "It seems to me Austria is the only place. We'll have to risk it. We have no choice."

"No, Shandor, I think we'll have a better chance in Yugoslavia."

"Yugoslavia? Impossible! Lisa, you forget the place is packed with Communists the same as Russia and there in Subotica everyone knows me. Don't forget we left there a year ago because they were looking for me and as soon as I appear on the street I'll be arrested."

"Wait a minute," she whispered. "You don't need to be seen on the street. We'll live in my mother's house, secretly."

"What do you mean? Go back to that life of staying in the house all the time, as I did before? It would be a life prison sentence without going to jail! There would be no possibility to work. How could we live? No, it's impossible! Remember, we had four months of that just last year!"

There we stood, two frightened people, on a street corner only a little way from the cozy apartment where we had been so comfortable until just a few minutes ago. Now we had nowhere to go. About that time I could have used a cup of the coffee we had left on the stove—something to drown my miserable thoughts. Oh, what have I brought to Lisa? What a jumble I have made of her life!

Lisa's voice broke into my thoughts. "Listen to me, Shandor. It isn't as bad as you imagine. It's only a temporary situation, believe me. We'll find a solution for everything. I'll work and make the living for both of us."

"No, Lisa, that won't do. We must think of something else," I protested.

My God, my God, what have I done? I thought over and over again, I've taken this wonderful girl out of her mother's home and made a fugitive out of her. What a mess I've made of our lives!

But Lisa was talking on and on. "My family will help us too, you know that. With Josep to think with us, we'll find a way. The most important thing right now is to save your life, and mine too. Please, this time do as I ask you, trust my judgment this one time, Shandor."

I looked at her. Here was I, who had been through many bad situations, many battles at the front where I had to make quick decisions in moments of great danger. Here was I, standing helpless while Lisa made plans to save my life. I felt I had come to the end of my rope.

"Time will solve all our problems," she continued. "Later we'll go to some other place, some other town where no one knows us. My family will do their best for us."

"No, I can't impose on your family again. That's impossible. Your brother has all he can do to take care of the family," I insisted.

"And there's your friend, Colonel Sokolov. The world situation can change overnight. I've often heard you say this, and we heard about the proposed agreement to divide Yugoslavia into two sectors, Russian and American."

"Oh, that's just a rumor. We can't put any stock in that," I argued.

"All we need is time," continued Lisa. "Time to hide and wait for the right opportunity. Please, Shandor, think about me. I'm the other half of this family, you know," and tears welled in her eyes.

We stood on the street corner in Budapest, our bags in our hands, looking at each other in this quiet night, while people were passing by smiling and talking, seeming to have not a care.

"Maybe you're right. We'll go back to Yugoslavia."

She kissed me and smiled through her tears. We walked to the railroad station and bought tickets to the village near the Hungarian-Yugoslavian border where we had taken refuge just one year before.

On the train I explained to Lisa everything that had happened that night between Morozov and me. Appalled, she listened to me without a word. When I finished my story I saw tears in her eyes.

"Oh, Sergei, Sergei," she whispered, "why didn't you listen to me? Why were you so reckless? You almost lost your life and I didn't even know about it. How could you keep anything like that from me?"

"I'm sorry, Lisa. I didn't want to frighten you. I thought..." I tried to apologize. Of course, she was right. With my thoughtlessness I destroyed everything that we had built with so much difficulty in Budapest. If I had only known, I never would have bought that car from Morozov. Feeling miserable, I looked out the window of the train at the beautiful Hungarian land; surely, for the last time.

XLVIII

We arrived at Antal-Bachi's house without any trouble. He was quite surprised to see us at his door, and when I told him the reason for our visit, he hesitated and said very slowly, "Well, I don't know how we can do it now. The situation here on the border has changed completely since you were here last year. We now have border guards on the Hungarian side also, although they are not as dangerous as the Yugoslav guards. There are not too many of them; and, most important, they do not shoot. On the Yugoslav side they have many guards with dogs, and they will shoot if they see anyone running. Many times we have heard shooting from there."

"I understand, Antal-Bachi, but we have no choice, we must try it, and I want to pay you for your trouble."

"No, my friends, I don't need your money. If you say you must cross over in these dangerous times, you must have very good reasons. I will help you all I can, but I want to warn you of the danger."

"Thank you, Antal-Bachi. I have a couple of questions. Can we get through the forest on the same path we used here last year?"

"Yes, you can, and I will go with you part of the way, but I am afraid it will be impossible to get through."

I looked at Lisa. "I have a plan and I think we can carry it out. Will you trust me?"

"Whither thou goest ... " and she smiled. A fine thing about Lisa, she could see the bright side of every difficulty and meet it with a smile.

"Now, Antal-Bachi, is your relative from Yugoslavia still in the same house near the border?"

"Yes, he is, but you must be very careful as there is a new patrol place, with a high observation tower."

"With reflectors?"

"No, still only for day use."

"That's fine. It works right in with my plan if we can stay here in your house for a few days, maybe a week."

"Son, you can stay here as long as you want. I'll tell my neighbors that you are my relatives here on a visit."

"Well, here's my plan. I think we can cross the border at night, but only if there is a rain, a hard rain storm with a high wind, something like the last time, for example. In such weather you cannot see or hear anything, and most important of all, the dogs cannot follow your tracks nor can they get your scent. Furthermore, I believe the dogs will stay inside during such weather. But now we must wait for a good rain with a strong wind."

Antal-Bachi laughed and remarked, "I think you will make it. I see you have had enough experience in such things, my young friend."

"Yes, the war trained me very well in many things."

"I can see that. Have you your rain coats?"

"Yes, we have them with us."

"All right, now let's eat. It's lunch time."

We waited at Antal-Bachi's house for more than a week. This was the fall of the year, when one could normally expect heavy rains, but during that time there was only one good rain and that happened in the day time. But, one night, when we were all asleep, I was awakened by a deafening clap of thunder. The wind blew and the rain beat on the windows hard enough to break them, it seemed.

This was the time! I wakened poor Lisa who at first couldn't understand what had happened and why she must get dressed quickly. Antal-Bachi knocked on our door. He was ready, and told us to hurry. The rain could stop any time. Antal-Bachi guided us to the border and we stood there for some time listening, but we heard nothing, except the rain and the wind. The patrol guards couldn't hear or see us, it was true; yet, we couldn't see or hear them, either. Suddenly, by a huge flash of lightning, I saw the big oak tree where we stopped to rest a year ago.

"Now!" said Antal-Bachi, and I took Lisa's hand and we ran across the road. In a few minutes we were by our tree, winded, but happy, as though seeing an old friend. I tapped on the trunk. "How are you, old boy?" We stood there a while leaning against the tree to rest. Now we were in Yugoslavia.

We continued our way through the forest very slowly, following our path and watching carefully ahead of us, because it was possible to meet a guard face to face. Suddenly my ears picked up a sound resembling a human voice just ahead of us. I grabbed Lisa and pulled her to the side as only three steps away someone was walking. We crouched down behind a shrub and I thought I saw a guard walk past. But, instead of another guard as we expected, there was a family with two little children, refugees the same as we. A child cried in a low voice, "Mama, I am afraid!"

They stopped near us and we heard one of the children cry, "I am tired, I can't go any farther." They sat down on the wet ground. The man was desperate. "I don't know what to do. I don't know which way to go to find the border."

Obviously, they were headed for Hungary. They were silently suffering, lost there in the middle of the night in a heavy rain storm with two little children. I couldn't stand it another minute.

"Hello. Don't be afraid. I am a friend," I said in a low voice.

The man jumped. "What? Who?"

"Quiet! Quickly! I will show you the way to Hungary. It is very near. We have just come from there." I carried the smaller child and Lisa took the other one by the hand.

"Follow us," and we started back toward our friendly tree. "Now, quickly cross the road, then go along the path about a half hour's walk, and you will find a village. My friend lives in the fourth house on the right. He will help you, I'm sure. Now run."

They started running and disappeared into the darkness.

We made our way again, slowly and carefully through the forest in the dark toward the house of Josep's friend. He, like Antal-Bachi, was very surprised to see our wet faces through his window. At the break of dawn, he took us to Subotica, hidden in his wagon under a load of corn cobs.

XLIX

Our trip to Subotica, luckily, was very short. Lying on the hard bottom of the wagon we felt every ditch in the bad country road. A dusty old blanket was our only protection against the corn cobs which were dancing heartlessly on our bodies. Lisa was just about to cry. I tried to shelter her with my hands and whispered again and again, "Just a little further, darling, and we will be home ... just a little further."

Our driver hurried his horses and periodically told us where we were: "Now, this is Bajmok Road ... Now, we are by the Big Church ... "

At last the wagon stopped and we heard quiet knocking on a window. Then a well-known voice asked, "Who is it?"

"Open the gate, Josep. I have something for you," answered our coachman. The gate opened and closed again behind the wagon. I knew we were in the court of Lisa's house. Then we heard, "Well, you can come out now!"

Slowly we rose from the corn cobs, as dirty and dishevelled as two hoboes. Josep stood by the wagon, astonished and without a word. Lisa's mother appeared at the door and exclaimed: "Lisa! Sergei! My children!" Folded in each other's arms, Lisa and her mother began to cry bitterly. As I looked at them I felt rather uneasy and unhappy. It was I who caused many difficulties to this family, and now I was here again. That could mean only new trouble for them. Maybe our decision to come here was thoughtless, made in rashness and panic. Maybe it would have been better to go some place else than to stay in Hungary.

"Welcome home, Sergei," I heard Josep say. "Mother, let them get out of the wagon. They need some rest."

Later we told our story to Josep and Mother. "I'm still not sure that we did the right thing by coming here, Josep," I finished my story.

"Of course, Sergei, it was the only reasonable solution. You couldn't risk your life and Lisa's by staying there any longer. I am very glad that you are here now in your home."

Josep tried to assure me that our decision was really a good one.

"And how about the Russians here and the police?"

"Don't worry, the last Russian soldier left this country a long time ago. We are an independent state now. The police don't know anything about you, Sergei. They really never knew anything about it. Their job was only to help Russians catch their deserters. Nobody ever bothered us again after that search. During that time almost every house here was searched for some reason, but no one even knew your name, Sergei. You may be absolutely sure that nobody knows that you ever existed, my dear invisible brother-in-law."

"But how about Lisa? What do the neighbors know of her absence?"

"Everything is all right, Sergei. She was visiting our cousin in Zagreb, and now she's back home. Any more questions?"

"No, no more questions, Josep. Everything seems to be all right. I hope we will not disturb you and Mother too much, living here in your home for awhile."

"Not at all, Sergei. It is also your home. There is plenty of room and you may stay here for a hundred years if you wish."

"Thank you, better not," I answered quickly, as everybody laughed.

L

Weeks and months passed as I lived, hidden, in Josep's house. Most of my time was spent in my room, coming out to the yard only in the evenings. Now and then I went for short walks, usually alone, following Josep or Lisa at a distance of a couple of houses. Lisa's family did their best to make my time less monotonous, and I really enjoyed the peace and quiet after those stirring days in Budapest. We had enough money, and Lisa was happy to be with Mother and me all the time.

The only thing that worried and troubled me constantly was the fate of my mother. "Where is she now? What is she doing? How is she living? Is she still in Siberia or back in Leningrad? Has my brother, Aleksey, returned from the army? Is he taking care of her? And, the most important thing, what does she know about me? Probably the army considers me as 'vanished during the war,' which means dead. Does my mother know that I am alive? Did she understand the hidden meaning in my letters to her from the hospital during my sickness?" I asked myself these questions a hundred times a day. Even in Budapest they were always on my mind, but I knew I could not write to her. I remembered very well that the Stalin's Law said: "The relatives of a person who escaped abroad shall be sent to labor camps, even if they didn't know about his intentions."

But I knew I didn't want my mother to think that I was dead, or let her worry and wonder about me forever. My only hope was Colonel Sokolov. To write him a letter was too dangerous, so I asked Josep to go to Beograd and explain everything to the Colonel.

Josep returned with very good news. The same day Colonel Sokolov wrote a letter to a friend of his in Russia, who in turn, would inform my mother about me. This 'channel' would be our postal service for the future, if everything went all right. As Josep finished his story, I felt a heavy weight had been lifted from my heart.

As time passed, my life in hiding began to be more and more unbearable. Our money was almost gone, and Lisa started to look for some work, as Josep's earnings were far from enough to support a family of four people. I became very nervous and tense and felt that I couldn't stand this kind of life any longer. The idea that I might have to spend many years waiting for some changes that may never come was horrible.

The news that the United States was not extraditing Russians back to Russia was encouraging. We regretted that we hadn't remained in Budapest in spite of the warning about Captain Morozov's searching for me. But who was to know the right thing to do? And how could we know that new rulings could happen so fast? Perhaps we should have gone to Austria that hurried, frightened night. From Budapest there was only one border to cross, and now we had two.

Thinking over this news, I felt that my only chance for freedom was to go back to Hungary, then to the U.S. sector in Austria. Lisa, of course, didn't even want to hear about it. However, I succeeded in persuading Josep to at least go to his friend at the border and investigate the situation there. I hoped we could go the old way again, walking through the woods to our old oak tree. Somehow I had confidence in the lucky tree. Josep agreed to investigate the situation at the border, and did so. However, he brought back only bad news.

"I was stopped twice by the patrol before I got to my destination," he explained. "It was just pure luck that I wasn't arrested. The second guard who questioned me was plenty tough. I told him I was going to buy a pig from a peasant, and he even went with me to the house where my old friend and buddy bore out what I said. He even regretted that he had none to sell me. They were all promised, he said. Otherwise I'd be bringing a live pig in here."

Josep continued, "I don't know how you can make it across now. I'm afraid it's impossible as there are too many guards, dogs, and watchtowers. Our friend told me that he very often saw guards accompanying people they had arrested. No one can go near the border now; he didn't know of any way he could help you."

"Do you think we could make it at night?" Lisa said.

"At night? I asked him that question too, but he told me there is now a barbed wire barrier in some places, and in other places wires are hidden which, when touched, fire light rockets illuminating the place. Sergei, it's impossible," and he heaved a sigh as he sat down.

"But this is the only way I know of to get to Hungary and then to Vienna, and I must go now," I said. "Who knows when that ruling may be changed again?"

"Yes, who knows? But it seems you must make up your mind to wait here for a better opportunity!"

"No," I answered, "if we stay here much longer it will surely be too late. I must get away now, at once. I must go even without our friend's help."

"But if you're arrested, they'll return you to Russia. You know that. You can't risk it."

"But what will I do here now? How will we live without work? Without an ID card? They'll catch me sooner or later. I must go now, risk or no risk."

"Sergei, I'm against it. Let's think it over. Maybe we can find some way out."

"Thank you, Josep, but I've thought it over and I can't wait any longer or it'll be too late. But now, of course, I won't try it with Lisa—I'll go alone. If I make it across I'll wait at Antal's house in Hungary until it's safe for her to come. I'll write and explain just when she should leave from here. She knows the way to the big oak tree, and I'll wait there on the other side of the line. When Lisa gets there by the oak, I'll run over and back with her. I'll ask you to go part way with her, you know, up near the border." I spoke with such feeling that the matter was settled.

"All right, I'll take her to you. I'll do what I can, but it's risky business," Josep said uneasily.

"Sergei, I'm against your plan. I don't like it. I don't want us to go separately. We must go together, everywhere, as we've always done. We made it before and we'll make it this time," Lisa assured me.

"But, Lisa, darling, I can't risk your life and liberty; I must look the situation over first, please understand me. It's true they might catch me, but it's better that they catch me only, not both of us," I pleaded with her.

"No, I want to go with you. If they catch you, they must take me too. I must be with you," and she began to cry.

"Lisa, you don't know what you're saying. I've told you before how difficult they can make it for a woman prisoner. No, I can't subject my wife to such a fate. You must stay here."

"Look here, Sergei," interrupted Josep, "why must you go just now, anyway? This new ruling of the United States is fine if you were only there in Austria, but since to get there is such an impossible thing, I think you should wait until the whole world situation is cleared up, which could be soon. I think you should be patient and wait for it. We can take care of you as we have, and Lisa will go to work too."

"Thank you, Josep, maybe your idea is good, but please think about my life, hiding, hiding, for perhaps a very long time. There's nothing certain, but I may be waiting here ten, maybe twenty years, maybe all my life, hiding," I pleaded.

"Sergei, don't be a pessimist. You know that time always solves all problems. Who can plan five or ten years ahead, in the condition the whole world is in now? We'll find a way out, I'm sure," Lisa said.

I saw that I was again defeated, since reason seemed to be on the other side. I reluctantly remarked, "All right, I'll think it over and we'll see what we can do. Don't cry, darling, please. I'll do nothing you're opposed to."

A few days later we discussed it again, as I couldn't reconcile myself to such a dark future. To live for years as though in a prison, and on Lisa's wages, without the possibility of moving out-of-doors for fear of arrest. Eternal fear of arrest would be worse than death. Again I explained all of this to Lisa and in the end we decided that I'd try—"only try" insisted Lisa —to go across and if I saw that it would be too dangerous, I would turn back. This time I decided to go by day, thinking the border guards would watch less during the day as all escapees tried at night. I took the binoculars with me. It might help.

When I was ready to go, a good friend of Josep's came to the house after dark with a wagon full of hay, where I would hide until we got to his home. From then on I was to be on my own way.

We said farewell and I could see Lisa was fighting back her tears. She looked at me and I could read in her eyes the question, "Will I ever see you again?" I felt terrible—some ill-fated presentiment gripped my soul and in that moment I saw my dear mother as she stood before me there in the deep snow in Siberia, whispering, "I will never see you again."

"Sergei," Lisa's voice pierced my consciousness, "once more I beg you, let me go with you. I can't let you go alone."

"Lisa, please ... you know I can't make it with you."

"Well, go alone but promise me again that you'll turn back if it looks dangerous," she sighed.

"I promise ... "

After hiding under the hay in the wagon I arrived at the home of our friend, which was near the forest. As soon as daylight appeared, I began to go forward very carefully. It was early spring. The snow was gone. The ground was wet enough that I could move almost silently.

The shrubbery near the path was naked, though, and there were no leaves to give me a good chance to hide. I started to go along the path but I noticed at once that it had been very much traveled. Obviously, it was the way used by the border patrols as I could see the prints of the big military boots. Coming down from the path I began to walk along beside it.

Suddenly, I heard a rustling sound and in a flash I flattened myself on the ground. A moment later two guards walked quietly along the path. This happened again a few minutes later; it seemed they were returning to the patrol house after their hours of duty.

My progress was very slow and I looked forward impatiently for the moment when I would reach our old friend, the oak tree. Suddenly I noticed something strange. It seemed I had reached the end of the forest, but where was the oak tree? I stood there looking and at last understood. Those damned patrollers had felled a broad sweep of trees all along the border and my friendly old oak was gone. I could see the stump and I wanted to cry for that tree. Yes, there was the barbed wire I had been told about and with my binoculars I could see other wires with light sockets. Near some bushes I saw movement and far away on the right I saw a patroller walking along with a dog. I had no choice. I had to go back. As soon as I felt safe back in the deep forest, I climbed a tree. With my binoculars I could see the barbed wire had come to an end not too far from me on the left. I climbed down quickly before I could be seen from the watchtower.

I decided to reach the end of the barbed wire going through the forest parallel with the wire. Periodically, I climbed a tree to see how close I was to the end of the wire. But I wasn't as near this point as it seemed to me from the tree. About two o'clock in the afternoon I was still walking, deep in the thick forest. Suddenly, there was a big glade in front of me. Standing behind a bush I began to inspect the other end of the glade for evidence of hidden patrollers. In that moment I detected a noise from the direction I had come. "The patroller with the dog," I thought. I had been in the forest too long and the dog had picked up my scent. There was nothing else to do but run across the glade to the barbed wire. I had to be close to the end of the wire by this time. I heard several shots coming from the right as the patroller ran after me through the forest. I reached the barbed wire and turned left running as fast as I could parallel with the wire. However, I still couldn't see the end of it. Instead, I saw another patroller running toward me. I looked around. In front of me and on both sides were the patrollers with dogs. Behind me was the barbed wire. I was caught in a trap like a wild animal.

"Stoj, ruke u vis!"* shouted the guards. I stopped. The guards caught up with me, and searched me and led me away to the patrol house where an officer began to question me.

"Name?"

"Sergei Sazonov."

"Birthplace?"

"Leningrad, U.S.S.R."

I know this time I had to, at least, give my real name and birthplace. During a half hour walk with the patrollers I prepared my answers for these questions. As I didn't have any identification papers with me, the most important thing was to establish my real identity. In that postwar time a man would lose his head very easily if he could not prove his identity. The European countries were full of various escapees—German war criminals, domestic quislings, and many others who, guilty or not, were escaping from somewhere or something.

"Residence?" continued the officer.

"Budapest."

"Why did you try to go to Hungary illegally?"

"To Hungary?" I repeated with pretended wonder, "I didn't want to go to Hungary, I came from Hungary," I lied.

The officer wrinkled his forehead. "Hey, you!" he called to a soldier in the next room, "send in the guards who captured this bird," and he stared at me. I looked at him very innocently, but was afraid he could hear the beating of my heart. "Oh, God, help me this time. Please help me ... not for me ... for Lisa and her family. Help me," I prayed silently.

The guards came in. "Yes, Comrade Commander?"

"Where did you catch this one?"

"Well, he was running along beside the wire, trying to reach the end of it, and, probably escape to Hungary ... "

"Yes," I interrupted quickly, "when I noted that the guards followed me, I of course wanted to go back to Hungary at the same place where I entered in Yugoslavia, by the end of the wire."

---

*Hold it. Hands up.

The officer looked on the table, where my belongings were that were taken from my pockets by the guard. Hungarian money, a restaurant bill, and a couple tramway tickets—all from Budapest —but nothing, just nothing from Yugoslavia.

"Give me your coat," he ordered me. He took the coat and looked at the label, "Made in Hungary." Then he sat back in his chair, shrugged his shoulders and filled out the form, "Arrested for attempting to enter Yugoslavia from Hungary, illegally." After that he signed it.

At that moment I felt I liked him—such a nice fellow he was—I wanted to hug and kiss him. He really didn't know what a great favor he did for me, for Lisa, and for my whole family. The police will never know that I lived in Lisa's house at all. If questioned, Lisa would say she knew me from the hospital, and saw me the last time in April, 1945 when I went to the front. Lisa and her family were safe from prison. Thank you, Oh God!

LI

At dawn on a beautiful spring day, in April 1947, I stood in a small yard of the Yugoslavia border house. There were about twenty of us, men, women and children, old and young, all of whom were arrested the day before for attempting to cross the border illegally. The border guards fastened our hands behind us, then tied one person to another. The small children were allowed to run free. It was pitiful to see them cling to their mothers or fathers, who were tied in such a way that they couldn't put forth a comforting hand to the little ones.

"Move!" commanded the guard and the column started to walk. The destination was the prison in Subotica. Investigation and trial would follow and who knew what would come later? After several hours we were walking down the streets of Subotica. It was still early and very few people were in the streets. "So here I am again," I thought, "a prisoner, where only a couple of years ago I walked as a Russian officer, but today—and tomorrow, what will become of me?" Complete despair overcame me. Why didn't I listen to Lisa and remain at home? Why didn't I keep my word and return when I saw it was dangerous to try to cross? Lisa, oh Lisa, no, it is not the end, no! The Russian Communists will never get me, never! As long as I am in Yugoslavia I have a chance, yes, a chance to escape, and escape I will!

"Stoj!" interrupting my thoughts was the raw voice of the guard. We stood in the yard of the prison. A quick roll call was taken and the receiving officer signed the papers. "Move!" he ordered and we were accompanied to a large cell and untied. The women and children were put in another cell. We did not see them again.

The cell where I was lodged had no chairs, no tables, nothing. Several old straw pallets were on the floor and two metal vessels called 'kiblas' were in a corner behind a curtain, which I learned was our rest room. The vessels were to be carried out and down to a cellar once or twice a day by the prisoners. There were two small iron barred windows and a metal door with a very small opening so the guard could look in on us. We couldn't see out as it was closed from the outside.

I sat down by a wall, closed my eyes and started to think. I had to be prepared for the investigation which I knew might come any minute. I had to have the right answers for every possible question in order to fight for my life. At the border I had told the guard who picked me up that I was coming from Hungary into Yugoslavia, and I felt sure the investigator here at the prison would accept that report. I could be almost sure they would never learn the truth about it and Lisa and her family would be safe. I knew I was in the hands of the O. Z. N. A. * who had the right to keep anybody in prison for months or years for 'investigation.' After that, the court would sentence the accused exactly as O. Z. N. A. would suggest to the judge, or if O. Z. N. A. should decide an accused was innocent he would be free without any explanations.

I also knew I would be a special case because I wasn't a Yugoslav citizen. They could simply extradite me to Russia without even a hearing, maybe within a few days. This meant I must do something to force O. Z. N. A. to keep me here in prison for a long time, during which I would find an opportunity to escape. Once in Russia, there would be no chance. They would probably shoot me the very day I was returned to them.

I needed time. Time was the most important thing for me now. But how? How?

I sat there in the cell on the floor by the wall in the crowded room, trying to think of an idea which would give the judge a reason to sentence me to a year or two in prison.

I had to hurry because I could be called for questioning any moment now. I had many ideas but had to discard them as fast as I thought them up, as they were impossible. At last I hit on something that might work, so I decided to try it. I would be insolent to the investigator, even to the point of insulting him, if I had to go that far, so he would want to keep me here just to punish me. I'd give him a couple of references who could give him plenty of reasons to sentence me. It could be Miklosh, the shoemaker, and ...

Suddenly the door opened and a guard stepped inside, calling in a loud voice, "Sergei Sazonov!"

"Here," I answered.

*Yugoslavia Secret Police

"Come with me!"

Heaven help me, I thought, as I got to my feet. Yes, I knew it. They would call me first. It wasn't every day they had the pleasure of arresting a Russian on the border.

"Have a seat," said the O.Z.N.A. officer and he actually smiled at me. He was a young man and seemed not too intelligent. His hands were rough and his blonde hair was rather unkempt. He was probably a peasant who had earned his title during the war among Tito's partisans. He started to question me and a secretary typed every word that was said. This officer was very polite to me, as a Russian ex-officer and one-time ally against our common enemy—Germany. However, that was exactly what I didn't want. I wanted him to be rough so I could hand it back to him and get him angry.

"And when the war was over my unit was stationed in Hungary," I continued my story. "Last year, 1946, the unit was demobilized but I didn't return to Russia."

"Why?" he asked quickly, "why not?"

"Well," I hesitated, "there was a girl, a very nice Hungarian girl ... you know, I just wished to stay here for a while."

"Oh, yes, I understand," he answered smiling, "but why did you try to cross our border just yesterday? Why were you entering Yugoslavia?"

"Well," I hesitated again, "you probably won't believe it but I wanted to visit a couple of Yugoslav girls, you know, just to say hello before I went back to Russia." I noticed that he started to lose patience.

"Are you trying to tell me that you came here only to say hello to a couple of girls?" he asked impatiently.

"Yes, that's my reason."

"This is your only reason for crossing the border?"

"Border?" I repeated, thinking to myself, now or never. "You mean you can still find the border? Very soon there will be no border!"

"What?" he asked. "What are you talking about?"

"About my country, Russia. There will be no more small states, only big Russia, huge, earth-encompassing Russia. We are the ones who liberated Europe from fascist Germany and all states will become republics of U.S.S.R. just the same as Ukraine or Byelorussia."

I saw his eyes blaze. It was working! He sat there and glared, very, very angry. "But make hay while the sun shines," I told myself. "Now I'll give him the last shot."

"And, please, if you will not permit me to stay here in Yugoslavia for a while, I ask you to contact my former military command in Budapest, right away. They will help me to get back to my country. I am not your citizen and I insist on being freed immediately."

He gave me a dirty look. "Just relax, young man. The war is over and you are in independent—yes, still independent—Yugoslavia. Your army is not here now and don't try to tell me what to do with you. You came here illegally, you know ... "

"All right," I interrupted him. "For this trespassing, you can't imprison me more than a couple of weeks legally and I ask you to contact the Russian Embassy in Beograd right away."

"Don't worry. We'll do everything we can to help you," he said sarcastically. He leisurely lit a cigarette, and, after a few puffs, asked the secretary to hand him the typed record. He slowly began to scan the pages. "You mentioned here that you knew some people in Subotica. Give me some names and addresses, please."

"At last," I said to myself. "I've waited for this demand for a long time."

"Of course," I answered and started to reel off, "The barber Steve on Main Square; Geza, a waiter at the "Three Hats" restaurant; Milosh Levai, a shoemaker, corner Freedom and Main Streets; the watchmaker, Kos, across from the railway station; then, oh yes, a few nurses at the hospital—Maria, a blonde. She lives in a big house to the left of the hospital, apartment 18; Lisa, Green Street, number 60; Vera Galic, Radic Street, number 15 or 25; Katerine ... "

"Stop! Stop! That's enough," interrupted the officer.

He pressed a button and a guard stepped in. "Take him away," he ordered in a loud voice.

Out in the corrider the guard directed me downstairs. "There, you ... " and I was put in a 'samica'* six steps long and three steps wide, with a pallet on the floor, a small window near the ceiling, a 'kibla' in one corner, and a jug of water in another. But I was glad—the success of my plan was my only thought as I paced from wall to wall. He doesn't like me. I'm sure he will do exactly contrary to what I asked of him. He will make every effort to punish me for my arrogant behavior to prove that he could punish even a Russian ex-officer.

*Cell for only one person.

LII

The days dragged on one by one with nothing happening and in solitary confinement, as I was, all I could do was think. I began to worry. After about two weeks the guard opened the door and commanded, "Out, for a hearing!"

As soon as I stepped into the interrogation room I began, "All right, officer, two weeks have gone by and I believe I am free now. I prefer to call my embassy rather than ... "

"Shut up!" he interrupted. "Read this," and he handed me a paper. I read: "We know this man in the photo. We saw him here in October last year." This was signed by two names.

"Well, now, you didn't expect this, did you?" He attacked in order to make use of my 'confusion.' "You gave me many names, but one of your references gave me these two names. You were here in Subotica last October too! You have crossed the border many times, illegally! Why! Answer me. Why?"

I stood there, silent. I thought to myself, all right, Sergei, he swallowed the bait. He has no idea that I led him to these two references, indirectly. Now he has a reason to keep me here and the judge will have a charge to sentence me. Everybody will be satisfied, including me.

"You have nothing to say now?" he sneered. "How about your two weeks and freedom? You can count on—let's see the law—you can count on at least one year for crossing the border many times. Very good, huh? Did you expect me to believe your stories about coming over just to say hello to some girls? You were here in October and I believe many more times, but you didn't even see any of them. Every one of your 'chosen' friends saw you here in April 1945 the last time, except these two, who are my witnesses!" This last, he practically yelled.

I thanked my lucky star they hadn't gotten any information from Lisa. She knew just what to say. To them, she was only another name among many others.

"I see," continued the officer, "you simply can't think up a good story in a hurry, but I'll tell you what I think about you—you are some kind of a small black marketeer, bringing something across the border. And—" he pointed his finger at me—"you may also be a spy, an imperialistic spy! I would rather believe that's what you are!"

A spy, my God! Now I am in for it. "No, I'm not a spy," I answered calmly.

"Well, if you're not a spy, tell me what you're selling and to whom, names and addresses. This way you can prove you're not a spy and after a short sentence you'll be free. Well?"

"I have nothing to say."

"Nothing? You'll be sorry. We have ways to force you to tell the truth," he finished with a threat in his voice. He ordered the guard, "Take him away!"

I was in my cell again, but this time I didn't know whether I was satisfied or not. "You have exaggerated your plan, Sergei," I said to myself. "I'm afraid you have outwitted yourself. I thought he would be satisfied to put me in prison for a while, but now he tells me I'm a spy!"

Now I was in a real predicament. I must get out of this, but how? O.Z.N.A. would do everything to force me to talk. My game with the investigator would not be as simple as I had thought. However, his words: "You can count on at least one year for crossing the border many times," were right now the most important matter for me.

Just then, as if in reply to my thoughts, a door opened and a guard stepped in with a pair of handcuffs.

"Is this for me?" I asked. He nodded. "They surely don't lose any time," I said as the cuffs clinked on my wrists. I knew the cuffs were a reminder to me that my life in prison can become a very uncomfortable one. As the officer said, they have many ways to force me to speak.

That night the guard awakened me. "Up. The officers want to see you!" And there I was again facing O.Z.N.A. officers. Next night it was the same, and the next. They tried to break me, quizzing me continually for about a month, yelling at me, "You lie. We know all about you. You are a spy for the imperialistics, for the United States and for England. We demand all information, names and addresses of your spy net."

I repeated to them again and again, "I am not a spy, not even a black marketeer. All I wanted was to see my girl friends and then to see the world before returning to Russia. My intention was to become a mariner in order to see India and Africa."

At last they tried another approach to force me to speak.

"All right, you won't talk. You will now go to your cell and remain there until you break your silence—days, months, maybe years, whatever you want. We have plenty of time," he finished and ordered the guard to take me away.

LIII

I remained alone in my cell, day after day, week after week. The food was very, very poor—a piece of bread twice a day and a plate of corn mash or cabbage soup, once a day. I liked the corn mash because there was some oil on it, but I didn't eat it, I put it on my hands and wrists, under the handcuffs. I discovered I could draw out my left hand, as my hands were rather narrow, and with oil on them it was much easier. This 'victory' against my enemies gave me great satisfaction. But one day the jailer came into my cell so suddenly that I didn't have time to get my hand back into the cuff and he saw it. The next time he came in he brought a chain, which he put on my hands; and he locked it with a padlock. An O. Z. N. A. officer stood by the door, watching. "Let me see," he said to the jailer and he carefully examined the chain. "Try it again," he said to me sarcastically.

The chain became part of my body. It was almost constantly on my hands as they tried to force me to talk. The jailers took the chains off my hands two or three times a day for a few minutes, but at night they were always on, tight, so tight that soon I had festering wounds where every link touched. I put the oil from the corn mash on the wounds, under the links. Many times I was so hungry that it was difficult to decide whether to eat the oil or put it on my hands.

However, I found a way to free my hands even from the chains. I could do it only in the evening when the guard took the chain off for a few minutes. When he put it on again, I widened my hands, just a little, but enough to steal one more link. That one more link meant free hands during the night. The jailers didn't notice it as the light was very poor in the cell and anyway they couldn't even imagine that I could pull my hands free. In the morning I put my hands back in the chains. No one can know the enjoyment I felt when I could move my hands right and left, up and down, freely! I swung my arms like a windmill, singing in a low voice: "Nam ne strashen seryi volk, seryi volk, seryi volk ... "*

The oil kept my wounds from becoming infected. Removing the chains during the night relieved the pain so I could rest. Before I went to sleep, I rolled the chains around my hands because the jailer looked in periodically.

Everyone in the prison wore his own clothes, no prison uniforms. The families were permitted to bring food and clean clothes in every day. It seemed to me that it was the rule in all small prisons in Yugoslavia. The O.Z.N.A. could refuse this privilege if they chose, but there was not much danger of that, since they saved a lot of money by having the food brought in. O.Z.N.A. used their right in my case, as a step to force me to speak. Lisa told me later that a short time after O.Z.N.A. quizzed her about me she started to bring food to me in the prison, but the guards refused to accept it. She said they always told her that there was no such person in that prison. She continued to bring food every day, along with other women bringing food to their men, but every day they told her I was not there.

After more than three months of having her food refused, she made up her mind to get some action and answered back, "Yes, he is here. I know it!"

"How can you know it when he is not here?"

"I know and you know he is here!"

Lisa was called to the prison office. An O.Z.N.A. officer asked her, "Why do you try to bring food to that man? You don't even know him very well."

"Yes, I know him very well. I told you before, I love him and he promised to return and now he is here. He returned to marry me!"

"To marry you? Crazy girl! You'll never see him again. He was here in Yugoslavia several times and he didn't even visit you."

"I don't care! Give him this food!" she demanded again and again.

The officer, disarmed by her stubbornness, shrugged his shoulders. "All right," and he called to the guard, "Give the man this food!"

It was a great day for me when I got the food from Lisa's home, not only because I was very, very hungry, but because I was

---

*Who's afraid of the big bad wolf, big bad wolf, big bad wolf ...

sure then that my family knew where I was. The feeling of the terrible loneliness was lifted from my heart. I felt that I could sing again, "Nam ne strashen seryi volk."

Lisa told me later that everyone was happy at home the day she returned and told them the food had been accepted.

LIV

Month after month passed, weary, lonely months. No one questioned me, no one spoke to me and no one was interested in me. The jailers were silent as if they were unable to speak or hear. Even my 'Good morning' remained unanswered. At this time I would have gladly accepted an interrogation by O. Z. N. A. officers just to have some change in my monotonous life. I suspected it was probably a part of their game to make me think I had been completely forgotten by the outside world.

Even so, I knew that O. Z. N. A. could keep me in prison as long as they wished.

My shoes had big holes in them caused by the continual walking from wall to wall, six steps forward, six steps back, hundreds of steps, I must have walked hundreds of miles. Hours and hours of walking and hours of thinking of only one thing: escape. But how? How? Many 'great' ideas came to my mind, but all of them were rather impossible, even foolish to think about. These ideas depended too much on the guards' carelessness, and I discovered that careless they were not.

I utilized every favorable moment in careful 'research' of customs in the prison, arrangement of the guards; times of change; the regular times for hearings; the times when there were the least number of guards on duty. Even the personality and character of each guard were important, whether he was strict and careful or good-natured and less careful. But most important was to study the prison building: arrangement of rooms, windows, doors, walls, roof and cellars. The most interesting objects were the weak points such as a rammed door in the cellar; locked doors in the corridor near the investigator's office; a small window in the kitchen, and the wall in the yard behind which was a demolished building, bombed out by the English aircraft during the war.

Each time I walked to hearings and back I discovered some

new details, and every day going out to empty the 'kibla' in the cellar was a good opportunity to observe. Being transferred several times from one cell to another also helped me in my explorations.

Of course I hadn't too many chances to investigate these spots carefully, but during a long time in prison many small, seemingly insignificant events might help in one's plans.

For example, it was forbidden to look from the window into the yard, and for this infraction the punishment was one day without a meal. After a couple of such punishments, I found that I could watch the yard and everything that went on there by using the tiny, high window, opened at a certain angle, as a mirror. With the help of this mirror, I discovered that not all of my 'great ideas' were just so stupid and impossible.

However, I realized that there was almost no chance to escape from O. Z. N. A. prison. The only possibility would be if I should be transferred from O. Z. N. A. prison to the second floor, in the so-called City Prison. The situation there was more liberal than in O. Z. N. A. prison. The prisoners were allowed to walk in the yard every day, and this walking became the main part of my escape plan. But I had to wait until I was transferred.

In the meantime, I still tried to find some other way to escape. During the day, my cell door was locked with only a latch but at night a key and the latch were used. I made a knife from the iron shank of my shoe, getting a sharp edge by grinding it against the rough cement wall. From two small pieces of wood which I tore from the window frame, I made a kind of fishing rod. With a string pulled from the covering of my straw bed, I tied one end to the rod and tied a loop in the other end. I listened for the footsteps of the guard. When he passed my cell, I pushed the cover of the peephole away with a tiny piece of wood and pushed the rod out. Hooking the handle of the latch with the loop in the string, I turned the rod and pulled the string until the latch was open. I practiced this exercise only during the night when I could hear the guards talking at the other end of the corridor. I hoped that only once the guard would forget to lock the door with the key, but that was foolish because he never once forgot.

LV

The idea of escaping occupied my thoughts during most of the long days and nights until I realized that constant thinking on one subject could harm my nerves. I was getting severe headaches, and my loneliness was unbearable if I allowed myself to dwell on it. I tried to find something else to think about and finally hit on counting everything in the cell that could be counted. The nails, or bolts, in the iron door ... there were twenty-seven hundred and ninety-six, four of them had been pulled out. The steps from wall to wall ... I added them as I walked hour by hour, transformed them into miles and calculated where I would be on this globe if I had walked in a straight line. I counted the windows on the court buildings, which I could see through my mirror window, and the grates on the windows and totalled them. I gave myself algebra and geometrical problems, which I solved with the help of my knife by writing on the wall. I made small chess figures from bread by chewing it and I sculptured the figures from the resultant dough. I dried them in the brief sunshine that filtered through my small window and colored half of them black with cigarette ashes which I found in the cell left by my smoking predecessor. I scratched a chessboard on the floor with the point of my knife and played for hours and hours.

A big change took place when I began to receive the food from Lisa. I looked at the food there before me, prepared by Lisa's own hands. She was so near, but at the same time she was so far from me. She lived only a few city blocks away, but it might as well have been on the other side of the world.

Looking at the basket of food—a small covered bucket of soup, meat or sandwiches and cake, wrapped in wax paper or a scrap of clean newspaper, or sometimes a chocolate bar—I began to think about another matter. There must be some way to establish contact with Lisa, some kind of secret correspondence. A connection of any kind could play a very important part in my escape and I must find a way to accomplish this. Days passed by I had not even the shadow of an idea. But one day as I sat eating chicken soup (my favorite dish) my eyes rested on the green paprika that had settled on the bottom of the little soup bucket. "I have it!" I yelled and jumped to my feet, spilling the soup on me.

I looked at the paprika with great excitement and love. "Yes, you will help me send letters to Lisa. You will be my envelope," I spoke to the paprika as if to a human being.

Yes, I would put my letter inside this paprika and send it to Lisa with the remains of the soup and she would send the reply the same way. The main problem seemed to be solved but how could I let Lisa know about this idea, this paprika letter carrier? And how could I write a letter without a pencil? I sat down slowly, saying to myself, "Easy, easy, Sergei. Just think a little more. You'll find the answer to this question too!" And I found it, or hoped I had found it.

This green chili paprika belongs to the Hungarian kitchen as, for example salt to any kitchen. It is used in almost every dish that is cooked: soup, vegetables and meat. I had taken a great fancy to the paprika and Lisa put some in the food she brought every day. It was usual to see paprika in the food the prisoners received from their families. Of course, the guards checked every basket of food that was brought in. Bread was sliced very thin, the same with salami, chicken and meat. They looked in the soup or sauce and stirred it with a spoon.

As the first part of my paprika plan, I started to send back to Lisa some of the soup in the bottom of the bucket, but without the paprika. I knew she would wonder, seeing it every day. She was accustomed to seeing only the empty container. After five days I changed my system. I left a paprika in it, hoping Lisa would begin to wonder why. And my clever Lisa, after three days of rejected paprika, took the paprika out and opened it and found a letter inside, a letter of one word, written out of letters I tore from the newspaper that part of the bread was wrapped in. I spelled out 'pencil' and glued the word on a firm piece of paper with sticky substance from the bones in the soup. Then I wrapped the 'letter' in foil that had come on the chocolate bar, and, making a tiny roll, put it in the paprika.

Next day when I found, in a paprika, a small piece of a pencil, I knew that the 'paprika correspondence' had been established. My first letter was written on a piece of paper three inches by one and one-half inches, with very small letters: "Darling, I love you. Thanks for food. I'm O.K. Hope you too. I'll escape. Need your help. Send address of friend where I can hide. Find out if there is a guard by demolished house behind wall on street side. Love to my wife."

The following day the 'mail man' brought a letter. Lisa was very, very happy and promised to find a place for me to hide and would let me know about the guard. "Everything is all right," she wrote. "Don't lose hope and don't forget to pray." No, I would not forget to pray. God was my only consolation during those terrible days and nights and I remembered the words of my mother at our last meeting, "Sergei, don't forget God and He will be with you always."

Our correspondence gave me new strength to fight; new hope for the future. "Now I'm not really alone," I thought, "and now I'm sure I'll escape."

My monotonous life received a shot in the arm and a pleasant pastime—reading. Thanks to our correspondence Lisa began to wrap my food in leaves torn from a book. I read these pages again and again until I received the continuation the next day. I finished this book in about two months and I knew it almost from memory.

One day I received Lisa's letter that soothed my tortured mind very much. She wrote: "We received Colonel's letter yesterday. Your mother is all right. She goes back to Leningrad soon. The army sent her a notice you had vanished in the war, but she knows you are alive."

My friend the Colonel did what he promised.

The summer months passed. Then came autumn with winter soon to follow. Sometimes I started to lose hope and deep despair took over. What if they really kept me here until I talked? Or what if they simply extradited me to Russia—say tomorrow—without a court hearing? What could I do? Such thoughts plagued my mind during those hopeless times. Should I try to escape now on some silly, but maybe lucky way, or wait for my plan? Usually these foolish thoughts seized me during a sleepless night, but when morning came I had regained my faith and trust in the future.

LVI

Six months passed by without any change in my prison life. It was quite a surprise when I saw the jailer open the door of my cell much earlier than usual. "Out for a hearing, you," he said crossly. "What is it now?" I wondered as I walked toward the office.

The investigator looked at me cautiously, probably trying to find in me some sign of yielding.

"Well, have you changed your mind?" he growled.

"I have nothing more to say. I've told you everything."

"All right, my friend, but we've lost patience and it's your own fault. Tomorrow you will go to Belgrade, to our central prison, and there you will begin to sing. I guarantee you they have many ways to make the people talk. Speak now or it'll be too late," and he banged his fist on the desk.

"I have nothing more to say."

He pressed the button so hard that he almost broke his finger, and a jailer took me out.

At least this will be some change, I thought in resignation, walking back to the cell.

It was nearly time for Lisa to bring the basket of food so I hurriedly wrote a note telling her I was leaving for Belgrade. Of course, she should continue to bring the food to the prison as usual.

The officer had told me the truth. Early the next morning a soldier came to my cell, chained my hands behind my back and conveyed me to a train. There we entered a vacant compartment and sat down, the soldier across from me. On the door of the compartment was a sign, "Reserved for Official Persons Only."

Upon arriving in Belgrade I was taken to the main O.Z.N.A. prison. The cell was about the same size as the one I had occupied alone in Subotica, but here there were eight beds, or bunks, and seven men. The door was the same, with a little aperture allowing the jailers to look in to check on us. The only difference was that in Subotica I could hear the footsteps of the jailers as they made their rounds from cell to cell, but here the jailers wore very soft shoes and I couldn't hear their approach. One never knew when a jailer was looking in on you which was a very uncomfortable feeling. The food here was much better than in Subotica. However, food could not be brought in from the outside. There was no one to bring it to me anyway.

The day after I arrived I was called in for questioning where an O.Z.N.A. major sat behind the desk. "Da cujmo tvoju pricu,"* he said ironically.

I don't know how many times I had repeated the story but it seemed never-ending. Wearily, but with all the control I could muster, I told it again. He listened to me, while he looked at my records, and when I finished he said, "Yes, exactly as it is written here. You have memorized it very well, my young man, but do you know what I'm going to do with it?"

"No, I don't," I answered.

"Look," and he began to tear it slowly into tiny little pieces and threw them into the waste basket.

"How long were you in prison in Subotica?" he asked.

"Six months."

"All right. You can begin to count another six months here. Of course, if you want to tell me why you were entering Yugoslavia, who you intended to visit and what your business was, we will permit you to go where you wish. Well?"

I said nothing.

"Very well," said the major, "you may go now. See you next year," he added, sneering.

I returned to my cell and to my seven cell-mates. They were very strange people—silent, reserved and rather unfriendly. No one introduced himself; no one asked me for my name. Lying on their bunks they stared at the ceiling almost the whole day, without a word.

After a few days one of them broke his silence when he heard that I could speak Hungarian. He was an ex-state prosectuor of Yugoslavia territory which was occupied by Hungary during the war. He told me a little of the rest of the Yugoslavs in the cell.

One was a journalist who wrote articles against Communism.

---

*Let's hear your story.

Another was an ex-manufacturer who refused to tell where he had hidden his gold and jewels when the government demanded it. Another was an ex-diplomat who had tried to escape the country. Next there was a colonel who didn't know why he was in prison. Another was a very old man, an ex-landowner, about whom no one knew anything.

Hearing these stories I remembered what Colonel Sokolov had told me about the Russian Revolution; these same circumstances prevailed in Russia after 1917.

While in this Belgrade prison with the seven others, all crowded in a small space, I thought of my cell in Subotica. There I was always alone excepting for a few days when the jailers brought so many men into my cell that there was not room to lie down—we had to sleep in a sitting position. At that time Yugoslavia tried to do the same as Russian Communists did in their country—to destroy the Kulaks* and to establish the Kolhozes.** The prison in Subotica was overflowing with Yugoslav kulaks who refused to deliver to the government their agricultural products and didn't want to join the Kolhoz. At these times the men who were crowded into my cell remained there only a few days. It didn't take a long time to question and condemn them—usually for several years in prison or to forced labor camps.

I felt as if I were somewhere in Russia, sometime after 1917, even though the happenings here were not quite so terrible nor in such great proportion. Yugoslavia had no Siberia to be sent to, but there were Goli Otok*** and stone quarries.

After about a month in Belgrade with my seven silent cellmates I was called again for the hearing. There was the same major who questioned me upon my arrival to the Belgrade prison.

"Well," he began, "we have lost patience with you, and you'll be extradited to Russia." He paused and leaning back in his chair surveyed me and continued, "You know, young man, I was present when we sent a party of about seventy men to the Russian Command at Horgos.**** I'll tell you what happened with them. These men

---

*Well-to-do farmers

**Collective farms

***Naked Island

**** A small city on Yugoslav-Hungary border.

were all good Russians, not runaways like you. They were soldiers and officers who had been captured by the Germans during the war, and put in concentration camps, and we all know what used to happen in those camps. These men would be killed sooner or later and they certainly knew it. The Germans promised them life and freedom if they would fight in the German Army. They agreed and were given German uniforms and weapons and sent here to Yugoslavia to fight against Yugoslav partisans. At the first opportunity they escaped from the German Army, went over to the partisans and fought with them against the Germans. They were very good soldiers and many of them became officers in the Partisan Army. When the war was over, they wanted to remain here in Yugoslavia or go somewhere else, but not back to Russia. There was nothing we could do about it as our Command had an agreement with Russia whereby we were obliged to turn their men over. We couldn't understand why those men objected so strongly to returning to Russia, their own country. We gave them very good recommendations but I guess these men knew Russian 'customs' better than we did. This extradition took place at Horgos, as I said. The men crossed the border where an escort of Russian soldiers waited for them. I was in our border patrol house when fifteen minutes later we heard machine gun fire. They were killed, yes, shot down in a little forest without a hearing or investigation." The major stopped, waiting for my reaction, but I said nothing.

"This is your last chance. If you tell us the truth we will let you free. If not—you are going back to Russia. Well?"

I was silent. What could I say? Nothing.

A few days later I was on the train on my way back to Subotica. As the train approached the Danube River a crazy idea came to my mind. I decided to jump from the window of the car into the river while crossing the bridge. I had seen this bridge on my first trip to Belgrade. There was a high fence, but I hoped I could jump between two posts and not hit them. When the train got to the bridge I asked my guard to take me to the toilet. Suspecting nothing, he accompanied me there. I closed the door quickly, opened the window and looked down at the river. Instead of dark deep water, I saw white ice on the surface of the river. How stupid of me! I had completely forgotten that it was winter already. Even if the ice had not been there, the water would have been much too cold to swim across the river.

LVII

There I was again in the Subotica prison. After a couple of days I received food from Lisa. Since my leaving for Belgrade, she was going to the prison regularly, asking about me. At last, the guards told her that she might bring food again.

My term started again, uncertain and endless like before. Week after week, month after month, the same dreary days. No investigation, no hearing, nothing. I could only walk from wall to wall, play solitary chess games, solve mathematical problems and think my thoughts. I read three more books, page by page. When will this end I asked myself over and over; there was never an answer.

But one day—it was more than a year after my arrest—I was called up for a hearing. I welcomed the change, but I dreaded the ordeal of facing the officers again. There could only be the same questions and my same answers. But this time maybe it would be different. Maybe they would sentence me. I dared not hope as I walked on leaden feet to the office. There he sat, my old friend the investigator, smirking at me.

"Well, our investigation is finished. We have concluded you are not a spy. Maybe, as you said, you really would only like to see the world, but you're going about it the wrong way, and of course, you'll be punished for it. You will be given fifteen months by our court. Twelve of them you have already served. Then you will be extradited to Russia as you have requested. To your regret, I might add, there are still the borders and next time I suggest you have a visa when you want to visit some of your girls."

I left the office, not daring to show my feelings. He thought he was a winner, but he was defeated. My plan worked. Fifteen months? Very good. I still had about three months to serve and that would be enough time to make my escape, I hoped.

Everything happened exactly as he said. A few days later I

was there in the courtroom. The court had three members, a judge and two assistants as jury. My case was heard in five minutes. The judge read my bill of indictment written by an O. Z. N. A. investigator, said something to the right and to the left assistants, stood up and told me I was sentenced to fifteen months, total, for the crime of illegal crossings of the Yugoslav border. After completing my term I would be extradited to Russia.

The next day I was transferred to the City Prison on the second floor of the building; just exactly what I expected. I was put in a big cell with about twenty other prisoners. Now I could begin to realize my plan for escape.

I already had the information from Lisa, the address of her cousin living near the prison who could permit me to hide in his home. She even told me where to find the key in case I arrived when no one was home. Yes, there was a guard on the other side of the wall near the demolished building, but only at night. This demolished building had been a part of the prison, but in 1944 American and English planes bombed the city several times and wrecked this part of the prison. "Thanks," I thought. "This is a strange coincidence! Many people died because of those bombings, but today they would bring about my means of escape." The wall was built as a temporary measure in order to enclose the prison yard.

The yard was surrounded by court buildings on two sides, the prison building on the third side, and the twelve foot wall on the fourth side. The men in the City Prison took their exercise walking in the yard once a day for about twenty or thirty minutes. Now I was one of them.

LVIII

I had known ever since I had been in O.Z.N.A.—now a year—that my only way to freedom would be over the wall. Many times I looked at that wall, through my mirror-window, thinking and counting. The wall was twelve feet high but if I would have a board about six feet long, a good strong board that I could use as a ladder, that wall would be child's play for me. But where could I find such a board? Pacing my cell I tried to recall every detail of my previous 'research work' in the prison. Yes, I thought, I knew where I saw such a board—down in the cellar. Very impatiently I awaited my next trip to the cellar to see if that board would be really good for my plan.

Every morning the prisoners made a trip to the cellar with their 'portable restrooms.' There was a drainage system where the kiblas were emptied. One by one the men came out from the cells; as one man appeared coming up the stairs another one started down, until the whole floor was finished. Everybody spent about a half a minute in the cellar. The guards watched the whole movement from the floor, but I never saw one of them even go downstairs. No wonder! That place was dirty and stinking.

There was a door leading into another room of the cellar, locked, of course, and rammed with two strong boards from the floor to the ceiling. Just what I needed, I thought, examining the boards carefully. The only problem was to try to take one of them down, because they were held in place by several large nails. I looked around for some kind of tool with which to pry the board loose, but there was absolutely nothing in the cellar. Then suddenly I realized I had the tool in my hand at that very moment, the edge of the metal lid of the kibla! I knew I could pry the nails loose with it but there was no time to try it at that time. The next man would be coming down the stairs any second and I must not raise suspicions by being in that place more than thirty seconds.

I could hardly wait until the next morning to start my plan in action. I emptied the kibla very fast and then started prying on the board with my 'crowbar.' I had time for only a few pries each day, but little by little the nails were loosened enough so that I could take the board down at any time. Of course, I put the board always in place with the nails pushed back in their holes, so that my work was absolutely undetected in that dark place.

I finished this work in about two months, knowing I must have that board loose and ready to move the very day I could see my chance to get away. I knew how I could escape, but when? Time and thinking solved that problem too.

Evidently, my sole chance would be during the exercise period and on a Sunday only, when the court offices were closed. During the week there were many officials and clerks in those offices. Any one of whom might see me climbing over the wall. Of course, there were two guards in the yard during the exercise. At the end of the walking period one of them led the line of men into the building and the other one marched in at the rear of the column. But I noticed a very interesting thing which happened one day during a fresh air period. Suddenly it started to rain. "Move into your cells," came the order and the prisoners began to enter the building, one after another. At the beginning and at the end of the column were the guards as usual. Everybody hurried because of the rain. When the last prisoner entered the building, the guard at the end of the column dashed into his guard room at the other end of the building, and after a few minutes came out dressed in a rain coat. But, during that time (two or three minutes) nobody watched the yard. I was in O.Z.N.A. prison when I noticed this thing for the first time, and during the summer I saw the same thing happen a few more times. During a sudden rain, every time, the guard would spend a few minutes in the building putting on his rain coat. The guard was sure every prisoner entered the building as he was the last one in the column. If I could be somewhere in the middle of the column I could go down to the cellar instead of going up the stairs. I had to do it in the same moment I entered the building. It was the only time when the guards from the floor could not see me, and the second guard would still be outside at the end of the line.

LIX

I still had one more month before the end of my sentence and before I would be extradited to Russia. My ladder-board waited for me in the cellar, and I knew where I could go, once over the wall. The time for my escape could be Sunday only, during our fresh air exercise, and only if a rain came during our walk.

This was the middle of summer, when one could not depend on the rain, though in this country unexpected showers often did blow in. But to expect rain, on a Sunday, at the time we were out-of-doors, was like asking for a miracle. Well, it rained last summer and it will rain again this summer I tried to tell myself—a drowning man clutching at a straw. There had been little rain in June and July, surely it rained some, but not at the time of our daily walk. It rained in the morning, just after our walk, in the evening, and sometimes all night, but never at the right time. I changed my plan. I decided to try to escape on a week day if it rained during the walking period. They would notice me from the upstairs windows as I ran across the yard with my board, but they would have to open the windows to cry out the alarm and that would probably be too late, as I would already be on the outside of the wall. Once over the wall they wouldn't catch me any more. But there was still no rain. Every day at the start of the exercise period I looked at the sky—not a cloud.

"Beautiful day, isn't it?" someone would remark.

"Yes," I'd answer, looking grimly at the sky.

Our paprika correspondence was cut down to a minimum. There were no more important things to write and I didn't want to chance spoiling the escape in the last days. It was almost impossible to write or read the letters in that cell with twenty other prisoners. One day during the dinner time I knew there must be a letter in the paprika because I felt something hard inside with my spoon. I pushed it aside and finished my soup, waiting for a chance to pull out the letter. Beside me sat a prisoner, some old Hungarian, eating his meal. He noticed that I pushed the paprika aside and remarked, "I see you don't like paprika. Give it to me. I like them very much."

"Oh, yes, I like them very much, too," I answered quickly and to prove it, put the whole paprika in my mouth and started to chew it. Believe me, that was a big stunt as that was a very 'chili' one. As the old man turned back to his meal, I pulled the letter from my mouth. It was really a very 'hot' letter!

The next Sunday was the same as all the other days. I could see even in the morning that it would be a beautiful sunny day. When we started our walk, I knew nothing could happen that day. But when we were in the yard, I looked as usual at the sky and noticed a big, dark cloud approaching slowly from the east.

"Oh, my God, help me. Help me now!" I prayed.

Five, ten fifteen minutes passed, nothing, not a drop.

"Come on, old boy, come on," I called silently to the cloud, looking, expecting and hoping.

At last! A few drops, then a quick heavy shower. "Move inside," the guard ordered and we started to go inside, one after another, as usual. I was about tenth from the end. As soon as I stepped into the building I turned left, downstairs to the cellar, instead of going upstairs. Perhaps some of the men noticed it, but nothing was said. Maybe I had my kibla down there, one could think. Anyway, nobody would think **that** was the way to escape. With only one good yank, the board was in my hands. A few steps and I was at the exit just in time to see the guard go into his room for the rain coat. Other guards closed the doors of the cells on the floors.

To run across the yard, put my board to the wall and climb up it, using the nails as ladder rungs, was a task of less than a minute. I jumped down and was on the other side of the street where everybody was running because of the sudden shower. I ran with them but not for the same reason.

"First street, second. Turn left, now right. Stop for a moment. This is the house. Nobody following? All right, get in," I ordered myself.

No one was at home, but the key was under the step, just as Lisa had said it would be. I entered the house and closed the door. I was free. I had escaped.

LX

It was incredible. Only five minutes before I was in prison and now here I was. It was so easy to escape, but to prepare for it! The agony of those hours, days and months of preparation! Lisa, where are you, Lisa? I would like to see you to tell you I'm here. Free! Free! Free!

But Lisa didn't come to see me for a whole week or more, even though I wanted it with all my heart. "Fifteen long months I didn't see Lisa," I complained to my host. "Why doesn't she come?"

"Be patient, Sergei, please," he tried to console me. "It would have been risky for her to come here now. I have a message for you from Josep. You know, we both work at the same factory. Their house is under surveillance, and the police raided the house the same night you escaped. The detectives are following every one of them and even their visitors. They also searched the houses of some of your relatives, but they never asked a single question of anybody. Lisa is continuing to bring your meals to the prison, and you know what they did? They accepted the food and brought back the empty buckets! I don't know who ate it, but I felt sorry about that—good food Lisa cooked for you. Fortunately, they stopped that dirty play after a few days and told her you were deported to Russia. She, of course, said she didn't believe them, and still took the food, back and forth like she did in the beginning. I hope they will be convinced she knows nothing about your escape." He finished his story.

I was the happiest man in the world when Lisa came in one last evening. Holding her in my arms I could hardly believe she was real and not just a dream. But, no, I was not dreaming, it was she indeed. I could feel her tears as they slowly rolled on my hands. I could hear her voice saying again and again, "You are here. You have returned to me ... " I could see her happy eyes, wet with tears, her face smiling, even though weary and worried.

She was very thin and pale. My heart ached; I hated myself because I caused her such suffering and torture.

"Lisa, it was wonderful how you handled the matter with the food." I tried to say something cheerful. "I can imagine how furious they were at you, but they were probably helpless wondering if you really knew something or if you were just making fools of all of them."

Lisa laughed. "Oh, yes, yesterday an officer called me in. I could see how mad he was. 'Why are you here again? Didn't we tell you he was not here?' he yelled. 'You told me the same thing last time and he was here,' I answered. 'Please tell me, Comrade, why won't you give him this food?' He didn't know what to say. He just looked at me. His face changed colors. Then he said, 'If I see you here again tomorrow, I'll put you in the same cell he was in. Now—out!!' And today, there is not a detective around our house and nobody followed me here!"

The news was excellent. However, we did not believe that O.Z.N.A. would forget me so fast. It was decided that I would stay in that home a few more weeks. Lisa and Josep visited me only occasionally, and only if they were absolutely sure they were not followed. I advised Lisa to establish an open house policy at their home: visitors welcome, doors open, act naturally as if they had nothing to hide. This was for O.Z.N.A. and for neighbors. Of course, no one knew who might be working for O.Z.N.A.

The young couple where I stayed worked all day from dawn until late evening, so I was alone always. The house was a duplex and I had to be very careful to make sure there was no noise during their absence. I couldn't even put a fire in the stove because the smoke could be seen from the chimney, so I ate mostly cold meals. When some visitors came, usually on Sunday, I would hide in the bedroom behind a huge wardrobe that stood in a corner. There I sat down on the floor until the visitors left.

LXI

Lisa would come once a week in the evening and on Sundays, when my hosts were at home. She would bring the dinner and enough food for a few days, and clean clothes for me. But one Sunday she didn't come at her usual time, and we didn't know what to think. At last we heard a knock on the door, but it wasn't she, it was Josep.

"Don't worry. Everything is all right," he said as he stepped in. "Lisa is fine now, just a little frightened and shattered, that's all."

"Frightened? From what?" I asked, alarmed. Josep sat down and told us what happened.

"It was about noon when she was on her way here, when suddenly she realized she was being followed by two men. She continued to walk, acting like she didn't notice them, but she carried a handbag with your lunch and clothes. She realized that if these two men stopped her, this would be proof that you are here in Subotica, and the proof that she knows where you are. What could she say if they stopped her and searched her bag? To whom was she carrying that food and clothes. She couldn't turn back and go home; they would stop and search her if she did. She walked along the street with the men following her at a distance. Thank God, she didn't lose her nerve and start to run. Well, she arrived at a place where several workers were building the walls of a new house. She went straight across the street to the building and approached the first man she saw. 'Hello,' she said in a friendly manner. Your wife was too busy to bring your lunch and she asked me to do it for her. You know we live near you in that big house. Here is your lunch, but please eat it quickly. I am also very busy today!' She sat down beside the worker, and he began to eat without question. Lisa talked to him and smiled. The detectives stood a while around a corner. Then they went away. The worker still ate his—I mean your—lunch, Sergei. Lisa was sitting on pins and needles wondering what would happen if his wife should appear suddenly with another lunch." And

Josep began to laugh. "Anyway, the lucky man had two lunches today, and you not even one. But L sa sent something for you, too," Josep continued, smiling, unloading his pockets. I was quiet, thinking about Lisa and all she had gone through today.

Obviously, Josep read my mind. "You can't stay here any longer, Sergei," he said. "I think it is about time you came back home."

"It is still too dangerous, Josep," I answered. "O.Z.N.A. can raid your house any time, and then ..."

"You are right. They can and probably will. It is their routine job, of course, but I believe they think you have escaped back to Hungary. Do you know how they searched our houses? They went from room to room, looking under the beds and in the wardrobes, in the cellar and attic. That was all. Let's think, Sergei. Maybe we can find some good place to hide you, somewhere they can't find you. For example, to divide a wardrobe with a partition, so you can hide behind it."

"No, they would notice that the wardrobe would be unusually narrow inside when they opened it."

"How about digging a hole in the garden? A small cellar with a strong top that one can stand on?"

"No, nothing like that. They may raid the house suddenly during the night. I wouldn't have time to get out of the house unless I stayed there all the time, in the hole ... " I smiled bitterly.

"Well, I don't know," Josep began, losing hope.

"Wait a moment," I interrupted. "You said a hole? Dug in the garden? Josep, if I remember right, there is no cellar under the rear part of the house? I mean, under our bedroom?"

"Yes, you are right, but ... "

"Just a minute, I think I have it, Josep! We can make a trapdoor in the floor of the bedroom. Two boards will be wide enough. After that, we can dig a small hole in the ground, only to sit in, no bigger. It must be near my bed, so I can jump in it in one second if necessary during the night. It must be close to the wall, where there is no chance of anyone walking on it. What do you say, Josep?"

"Excellent. I knew you'd find a way, Sergei. Lisa and Mother will be happy to have you home again. I must hurry now to tell them the news. Oh, yes, one small correction in your plan, brother. Not we ... I myself will do the job. You must stay here until it's finished. Now, let's see your plan in detail so that tomorrow I can start to work on our project." Josep was completely animated, but so was I.

LXII

The hole was finished in one week, and Josep came in the evening to take me home. As usual, he walked first and I followed him at a good distance. It was a long way, and I sighed with relief when I saw, at last, our home. The house was dark; only one window lighted—the sign that everything was all right for my arrival.

There I was, in the home I thought I would never see again. Lisa, Mother and Josep—all my family—were there, telling me warm, comforting words. Dinner was being prepared and the table was set for four people. I looked around. Nothing had changed since I was here last time many months ago. Even the cat welcomed me as though I had never left.

"Come here and see my work," Josep was pulling me into the bedroom.

"Can you see it?" he asked proudly.

I looked at the floor where the hole was supposed to be. "No, I can't," I admitted. I could see only flat floor, covered with a carpet. "But I know it must be here," and I pointed to a place by my bed, near the wall.

"Yes, it is here. I did it exactly as you told me, with a few small additions," said Josep, lifting the cover of the hole.

He really did a very good job. The edge of the carpet was nailed to the cover so it could be opened and closed without moving the carpet. It was impossible to notice anything on the carpet surface. The hole was big enough to sit in and boards covered the walls and floor of the hole. A few pillows were lying inside to make my 'room' more comfortable.

I jumped in, sat down and closed the cover. Complete darkness surrounded me. I felt cold, and an unpleasant musty odor was coming from the wet ground behind the boards. Above my head I heard voices and steps, but I couldn't understand the words. "Burr . . . !" I thought, shivering. "It is like a grave!" I quickly opened the cover.

"Well?" asked Josep impatiently.

"Perfect job. My congratulations." I was really satisfied in spite of my uneasy feeling in the hole. "And what about the dirt?"

"I spread it around in the garden. Nobody can even notice it. We worked in the dark, of course."

"Very good, Josep. Now, only one more thing left. Let's play a little game. Say like police and gangsters—Josep, you are a policeman. Go outside and knock on the door. Mother, you will open the door for the police, please, but stay here, close to the door, so you may open it quickly. Lisa, you are the director. See that everybody plays his role well. I am, of course, the gangster, who robbed a bank, let's say."

I returned to my room, closed the door and turned off the lights.

"Everybody ready?" commanded Lisa. "Start!"

I heard the knock on the door and Josep's voice: "It's the police. Open the door!"

Hurrying across the room I could hear Mother opening the door. Damn it! I fell down, making a loud noise, smashing into something on my way.

"Hands up. Surrender!" Josep said as he stood in the room with his finger pointed at me.

Everybody burst into laughter while I sat down on the floor, rubbing my knee, and looked angrily at the small hassock beside me.

"Once more! Everybody in his place!" Obviously the director was very dissatisfied.

The second try succeeded without any accidents. When Josep came in the room, I was already in my hole. Now, we were prepared for a real performance.

We didn't have long to wait. They struck one night, surrounding the house and knocking loudly on the door. It awakened me immediately, and I simply got out of bed and into the hole, which was already opened. They searched the house in the usual way, and left quickly without a word. Lisa opened the cover to the hole and I was glad to get out. We lay there in our bed silently, thankful they were gone and wondering when the end of this miserable life would come.

The O.Z.N.A. raided our house twice in the next three months. In both cases, they came during the day, making a rather quick and cursory search. Even so, it was hard on our nerves and it kept us under continuous tension, day and night. I, myself, would jump from my bed at every little sound I heard outside during the night. Many times it was only our cat, or simply the wind blowing.

The visitors were giving me a very hard time also. I think, this was the time when I developed my complex against uninvited guests. Fortunately, it was the autumn of the year and we tried to stop the open house policy, but our good neighbors, friends and relatives never understood why they were not so welcome as usual in this hospitable house. They would sit for hours and hours, chatting without end, while I was cramped in the dark hole, freezing to death. The children were the biggest problem. They would wander in our bedroom and skip and play above my head like little demons. Lisa finally put a heavy chair on the cover, so they could not discover my hole accidentally. It was a most unforgettable enjoyment to get up out of the hole and stretch my twisted bones as the last stubborn visitor finally left.

Life became a little more tolerable as the O. Z. N. A. stopped their raids on our house. My other enemy—visitors—were defeated by cold winter and snow, and by using old tactics: "Nobody is home" or "Lisa is very sick and it could be something contagious" or "Josep is sleeping, please speak quietly, " etc.

Lisa had been working in a stocking factory since the time I was arrested; a part of her earnings went for the food she brought me in the prison, the other part was for the household. She and Josep were the breadwinners for our family. Mother and I were at home. What else could I do?

LXIII

Six months passed by since I escaped from the prison, and I was still here, in Lisa's mother's house—a prisoner without a prison, a man without hope or future. I felt that all doors to freedom were closed to me, for now and for always. It was only too clear to me that I must never risk crossing the border again. This meant I was forced to stay in Yugoslavia whether I liked it or not. But it was impossible for me to accept this kind of existence: hiding in that hole for the rest of my life—maybe for years and years; depending upon the earnings of my wife for the very food I ate; forcing every member of the family to live in extreme fear of arrest and prison. This was indeed a very dark picture. No, I could not reconcile myself to such a fate. I had to find a way out.

At the first sign of spring I began to think with renewed vigor of some solution to my terrible situation.

The most important thing in Yugoslavia at that time was still an ID card, or "Legitimacia." Without an ID card no one in Yugoslavia could travel, rent a room, or apartment, or procure food ration cards. In a word, no one could live in Yugoslavia without this magic amulet.

Many times I imagined how convenient it would be if only I had such a nice, blue ID card. I could go with my Lisa very, very far from here to some place where nobody knew us. But I didn't have it. Unless I myself would produce one, using somebody else's card, I thought, holding Lisa's card in my hands. "All right," I said to myself, "let's see what can be done about it."

I talked it over with Lisa and she brought me about half dozen ID cards which she borrowed from her trusted relatives, sisters, in-laws, and grandparents. There was no danger to them if I destroyed one or two of the cards. They could go to the police and claim they lost them and receive a duplicate.

Looking over these cards, I came to the conclusion that it would be possible to alter a card in such a way I might use it as my own "Legitimacia." In order to make a perfect 'fake,' I had to do three things: one, unglue the photograph and put on my own picture. Next, erase all information and fill in my data. And the last was to produce some kind of stamp, to seal a corner of the photo as it was sealed on every ID card.

To unglue the photo was easy, using the same technique I had used as a child when working with my stamp collection. I put a damp cloth on the photo and pressed it several times with a hot iron, and the photo was unglued. But the second task, erasing the ink, was not so easy. It would be too noticeable to simply erase it with an eraser. It had to be done with some kind of fluid that would wipe out the ink without a trace, yet not change the color of the card.

For the purpose of my research work, I opened a small 'chemistry laboratory' in a drawer of Lisa's dressing table. Everything in the house was at my disposal. The whole family was ready and willing to run out and get anything I needed. I mixed various fluids in many different ways; lemon juice, vinegar, alcohol, household cleaners—everything I could think of, but I couldn't find the magic formula. I succeeded in dissolving the ink, making it disappear; however, with it went the paper, completely destroyed.

One day as I worked in my laboratory, I soiled my white shirt with ink. Not wishing to be chided, I hid the shirt and forgot it. Later that week, while putting on a clean shirt Lisa handed me, I noticed it was the same shirt I had hidden, but now it was clean, no sign of ink.

"Lisa," I shouted excitedly, "Lisa, how did you wash this shirt?"

"I didn't, Mother did. Why?"

"Mother—where is she?"

"What is it, Son?" she called from another room.

I ran out to her. "Mother, this shirt—how did you do it? There was ink on the sleeve. How did you get it out?"

"Very simple, Son. With bleach."

"Bleach, what bleach? Where is it?"

"In the washroom, of course. Why are you so excited?"

"Please, Mother, show me this bleach and how you washed out that ink."

"Son," she laughed, "come with me and I'll show you how to wash, if that's what you want."

From the shelf in the washroom she took a bottle of a white powder, handed it to me and gave me directions for using it as it was very strong.

"Thank you, Mother, thank you very much." I kissed her and went to work at once. After many tests on several pieces of paper, I found I had my magic formula. A simple laundry bleach! The writing disappeared from the ID card, leaving it clean as if nothing had ever been written there. Only the signatures of the police chief and stamps were on it. I experimented to see how it would look if I wrote on the bleached part. As I began to write, the ink began to fade and after a few seconds disappeared entirely. I saw that the paper had absorbed the bleach and dissolved the ink again. I started to write again but it was no use. The ink spread out on the card, ruining it beyond salvage. I destroyed the card and set to work on a new one. Several days passed without a solution. It was clear that the bleach would dissolve the ink, but at the same time make the paper impossible to hold ink again. This was a bitter disappointment. I had felt that I had freedom in my hands. But now—nothing.

I thumbed through the rest of the ID cards and was struck with the idea that perhaps I could use one of them as my own by changing only the photograph. I found a couple of them that might serve the purpose, but the dates were all wrong. I couldn't use one which stated that I was sixty years old or one that said I was sixteen. At last one of them held my attention. It was the card of Lisa's unmarried sister, Ivanka. If I could dissolve the last two letters from her first name, it would not read: Mezei, Ivanka (a female name), but: Mezei, Ivan (a male name). I checked the other data—hair, eyes, nose, face. Everything was satisfactory. Date of birth I could manage as there were only three years difference. But the sex! Well, I could correct that too. In the Yugoslav language the words 'male' and 'female' are very much alike, so I managed to change the word 'female' into 'male.' "Anyway," I thought, "I don't think any policeman checking over my card will notice it and he wouldn't doubt my sex, I hope."

I could start my work again; but before it could be of any use, there was another hurdle. I would be obliged to obtain an Odjava* as at that time everybody in Yugoslavia who wanted to move from one place to another was required to secure this notice from the police, stating where he wanted to go. When he arrived at a new address he must notify the police and receive a Prijava. ** Without

---

*Notice of Departure

**Notice of Residence

this notice he could not even rent a room. This was one of their methods of keeping track of everyone.

I asked Ivanka to get this notice as soon as I could decide on a safe place to live—some small town—but it must be very carefully chosen. The best thing I could think of was to read the newspapers regarding employment, but I wanted papers only from Croatia, for two special reasons. One, because Croatia was the part of Yugoslavia which had frontiers bordering Austria and Italy. I wanted to live close to the West in any event. The other reason was I felt it safer to live where no Hungarian minority lived. According to the ID card I would be carrying, I would be a Hungarian. It would be normal that I be expected to speak Croatian with a Hungarian accent, but every Hungarian would immediately know that I was not really Hungarian. So it was necessary to avoid conversing with Hungarians.

LXIV

I read the papers every day for several days until I found something I knew I could handle. A firm in Samobor, a small city in Croatia, advertised for office clerks. **Samobor,** I noticed, is very much like the name of another city, **Sombor,** which was near Subotica, and I thought it would be an easy matter to change Sombor to Samobor on my papers so I could not be traced. All right, I'll try it. I sent a telegram asking if the position was still open. The answer was in the affirmative with an application form attached, and a few days later the job was mine.

This was not unusual, as at that time Yugoslavia needed many clerks as the new Communistic bureaucracy was setting up quite a program. The time for starting my new job was settled for the first week in May, 1949.

The next thing was to send Ivanka with her ID card to get the Notice of Departure to **Sombor.** Everything went smoothly and the notice was in my hands the same day. Now to start to work again, to change Sombor to Samobor, so that my departure could not be traced. A few weeks later, Ivanka would go to the police declaring she lost her ID card and Notice of Departure. If the police should check they would find that no one with that name had registered in Sombor.

Now I began to work on 'my' ID card to dissolve the letters "ka" and unglue the old photo and glue on the one which Josep had made of me. The last job was to make the same kind of stamp which was on the ID card to cover a corner of the photo. I noticed on other ID cards this stamp was not very visible, rather just a remainder of a stamp as everyone was obliged to carry the card at all times. Naturally the stamp looked quite worn. There was no other way to transfer this stamp to the new photograph except to write the letters inversely and press it on the photo while the ink was still wet. Of course, a great deal of time was spent before my stamp imitation became passably fair, and in the process, I ruined several photos. At last I accomplished this feat. I showed the card to Lisa and the family, proud of my masterpiece. They were all surprised. Lisa, who hadn't thought much of the idea in the first place, changed her mind and told me that with that card I could go anywhere in the world.

Lisa decided that I should go to Samobor alone; and, as soon as I was settled, she would follow. A few days before May, I left the house and walked to the first railway station outside of the city, thinking I might be less noticed in a small station than in the main station in the city of Subotica. It would have been difficult to recognize me because I was wearing dark glasses and a mustache. It was possible that the police had forgotten about me long ago, thinking I had escaped to Hungary; but, of course, I couldn't count on it. So every precaution had to be taken.

I was greatly relieved when I finally bought a ticket to Samobor without mishap. However, I didn't breathe freely until I got on the train and felt it moving. I was tired mentally and physically; and, as it was night, I fell asleep almost at once.

I don't know how long I slept, maybe a couple of hours, when I was awakened hearing, "Comrade, hey, Comrade, wake up!" and a hand shook my shoulder. I was paralyzed with fear as I looked up and saw a policeman. "Your ID card, please!"

"My ID card?" I repeated stupidly.

"Yes, your ID card. Wake up!" and he laughed, thinking I was still asleep.

At last I understood where I was, and said, "Oh, yes. Sorry, here it is."

He looked at the card and at me. "All right, you can go back to sleep," he said as he handed back the card.

I closed my eyes, but didn't sleep. I had just gone through the railroad police control and my ID card passed its first examination. With great difficulty I controlled my trembling and continued to sit with my eyes closed, not wishing conversation with other travelers. Some time later there was another police inspection, but not the same officers. Would this suspense never end? I gave them my card and everything went smoothly, not even a question, though I noticed they questioned other passengers regarding names, places and dates. My relief was indescribable. When I got off the train in Samobor and strolled down the platform through the train station, trying to appear nonchalant, but inwardly quaking, a huge lump was in my throat. And now, as Ivan Mezei, with my fake ID card in my pocket, I began to breathe free air, the first in a long time.

LXV

As I walked through the pretty little town which was surrounded by hills covered with green forests and dotted with tiny church spires here and there, a feeling of peace came over me. I became aware of the streets lined with blooming chestnut trees and flowers growing in private gardens. Perhaps after all this was freedom and security. Perhaps I wasn't dreaming.

The green-lawned town square was encircled by substantial buildings: a bank, post office, stores and the inevitable coffee shops, but it was early morning and they were not yet open for business.

While walking down the main street, I came to an old stone bridge spanning a stream, Gradna Potoc, a little river flowing down from the hills and singing its way through the town and on down the valley to join the Sava River, some miles below. I stood on the bridge listening to the peaceful rippling water in this quiet town dreaming of the day Lisa would join me and we could begin a new life, a free life. It seemed I could stretch out—my mind, my body, my feelings. I experienced a wonderful sense of freedom from the torturous months of hiding, haunted by constant fear and agitation. A feeling of rest came over me, such as music brings.

As I stood there in this beautiful spot, waiting for the coffee shop to open, other thoughts raced through my mind. What can I expect here in this quiet town? Will I live here a short time or a long time? Will they arrest me again? Will I live to be an old man and die here as Ivan Mezei, with no one knowing who I really am? Will I be in a position to see my mother again? This was a good joke on me—this irony fate has handed me. I escaped from a Communistic country at almost the price of my life, only to run to another country which had been taken over by the Communists. (Maybe this will not be my last stand, though. Maybe I'll succeed in my escape from Communism).

But I had no time for irony or bitter reflections. I had things to do which required all my energy and alertness. It was six o'clock. The coffee shop was open.

A few minutes after seven o'clock I presented myself at the office where I was to work. Everything went smoothly and I was given a note certifying that I was engaged for office work at that firm. After that, I went to the police to report my arrival. Again there was that old fear. I tried to act naturally as I handed the police the ID card, my Notice of Departure from Subotica, and the admittance to the job.

Words—there are none—to describe my feelings while I waited for the clerk's scrutiny of my counterfeit ID card. After a few minutes, he handed back all cards stamped with the official approval. He directed me to the City Hall where apartments and rooms were distributed to new residents.

Fortunately, there was a room in a house near my office. About noon I stood in a small room, rent paid in advance. I, Ivan Mezei, was a new resident of Samobor.

I lay on the bed and began to think of my new life already begun. I have my work, a room to call home. Only yesterday, I was a prisoner, hiding in a hole under the house, without a ray of hope. Life was really very strange!

Now there was only one more thing to do: to have my Lisa with me. From that day on, I put my mind steadily to my work on looking for a way to arrange for Lisa's coming.

LXVI

After a couple of months, a girl in my office was transferred to another office and I asked my chief if he would give the vacancy to my wife. He agreed. At the same time, he complimented me on my work, saying it was conscientious and accurate. He never knew how earnestly I applied myself to my work. He didn't know that my very life depended on my holding this job.

Even though Lisa had not had training in office work, I knew she could do it as well as I. It was very simple for anyone who could read and write and count; and, as the vacancy was on the desk beside mine, I could instruct her if necessary.

I wrote Lisa at once telling her to do just as we had planned: to ask for the Notice of Departure to Sombor and to come to Samobor. I would have to make the necessary changes on the document so the police here would give her the residence permit. According to our ID cards, we were Ivan Mezei and Lisa Mezei, husband and wife.

A few days later Lisa was with me, and we began another 'new life' together, but this time with a certain amount of assurance. And we were happy—very happy. We could forget our fear of tomorrow and make plans for the future. We were in perfect agreement about our work. It must be perfect, with no disturbance to other clerks, keeping as quiet as possible, attracting no attention.

One of the important things to do was to become accustomed to my new name, "Ivan." At first it was very difficult to answer to the name, the same as it had been in Hungary where we had to learn I was "Shandor." Again we practiced at home and on our walks in the parks and in the hills above the town. It happened many times that Lisa or someone else had to call two or three times, "Ivan, Ivan," before I answered. Those around me began to think I was a little hard of hearing.

During this adjustment period, we stayed to ourselves as much as possible, refusing invitations to private homes. We were both good dancers and enjoyed going to the town dances.

We earned very small wages and we were very poor. I had one pair of shoes, one suit of clothes, no winter coat or heavy shoes, and winter was just around the corner. Lisa was a little better off than I. She came from her mother's home fairly well outfitted with wool clothes and fur coat. Before winter set in, by careful planning and management and counting pennies, we bought, in a second-hand store, soldier's shoes and a short winter coat for me, and wool stockings and gloves for both of us.

As for household items, we needed everything from teaspoons on up. We had been eating in the Menza* where the food was not too good, but of course much better than the prison food I had eaten in the past. Lisa's mother sent us packages of food about every two weeks, smoked meat, bacon, flour and sugar. This was really 'manna from heaven' and it gave us a chance to cook our own meals once in awhile. Needless to say our 'home' was one room, but we were so happy to have it and each other, that to us it was a palace. Lisa had brought some household linens, which she had made years before, and with her knack of fixing things, we were quite cozy.

My Russian accent was considered to be Hungarian, as everybody thought I was, with my Hungarian name. One could hardly know the real nationality of a man only from his accent.

---

*Workers' kitchen

LXVII

As Lisa and I didn't travel anywhere, there was no danger of having to show my false ID card. In the small town, like Samobor, everyone knew everyone else, and soon I knew every local policeman by his name. No one even asked for my ID card and though I carried it in my pocket at all times, I had practically forgotten about it.

One day in 1951 Lisa met me during the lunch hour with fear in her eyes, asking quietly, "Have you read the papers today?"

"No, I haven't. Anything serious? Let me see it!"

"No, no, let's not be seen concerned about it. I'll tell you about it and you can read it later. They're going to change all old ID cards for new ones," she whispered.

With an effort I controlled the expression on my face, but here was the old fear right back, staring at me and taking complete control.

"My God, Lisa, what will happen to us now? You're right, we mustn't be seen to be too concerned. We'll go back to work now, dear."

Easy to say, 'go back to work,' but how could I put my mind on my exacting work, with almost certain detection facing me. With my thoughts in a whirl, I somehow managed to pretend to be doing my work until quitting time.

On the way home I bought a newspaper and nonchalantly put it under my arm without looking at it. Quickly Lisa and I did our marketing and hurried home where I read the bad news. All old ID cards were to be changed for new ones for all citizens of Yugoslavia, beginning the first of next month.

Pacing the floor and thinking aloud I asked, "What will happen now? Will they notice my false card or not?"

"No, they will not!" Lisa said in a firm voice.

I looked at her. She stood by the stove cooking our evening

meal. Without looking up she continued, "You and I both know you did a very good piece of work on that card, and it has passed three times;twice on the train coming here and when you registered at the police station after ... "

"But this is different ... "

"No different at all, maybe even less dangerous. I remember when I received my first ID card in Subotica, there was such chaos, a mass of confused people, and busy clerks. Your card will be one among thousands of others, and nobody will even have time to take a good look at it."

"Lisa, you could be right," I remarked as we sat down at the table, but, tempting as Lisa's good cooking was, I couldn't eat. That old fear was back again, weighing me down. What must I do? Take a chance? Abandon everything and go back into hiding, return to the hole—the dungeon, I called it—with never a hope for the future? I tried to keep my desperate thoughts from Lisa because she was putting on such a brave front.

The days passed and the time for us to appear for our new cards drew near. I knew I had not the strength to return to that damned hole under the floor. In horrible suspense I lived through the days trying to appear unconcerned and doing my work as usual.

Finally we received the forms to fill out with the necessary data. The day came when we had to go to the police station to receive the new cards, along with others whose names, like ours, began with M. Always the police, police, police—would I never be free of them?

As we stood in line, I looked at the others and wondered if any of them were nervous for the same reason that kept my insides churning.

At last we entered the room and signed our names in front of an officer, acting as coolly and naturally as everybody else. We gave him our old cards. He looked at them briefly and put them in a file. We signed our new cards, and our fingerprints were put on them. "Next," called the officer, and we came out.

I looked at my new, my beautiful ID card and I couldn't believe my eyes! Now I never have to be afraid to show my card. We could even travel now.

As soon as we left the police station and were out of hearing of anyone, I grabbed Lisa's hand and almost yelled, "Come on, Lisa. We're going to Zagreb!"

"Now? Why?"

"Yes, now, right away. Just to travel as other people do.

Just to see Zagreb!"

We had lived in Samobor nearly two years without ever being out of town. Zagreb, the capital of Croatia, was only twenty kilometers away; but to travel meant to show our ID cards, and we had never dared.

The pleasure was indescribable to sit with Lisa beside me, in the small car of the small train and travel. It was an even greater satisfaction to show our ID cards to the police, who, as usual, checked all passengers.

"This year we will go to the sea on our vacation!" I whispered to Lisa.

LXVIII

However, we couldn't go to the sea that year, nor even the next year. This time it was sickness that I had to fight against. Pneumonia as a consequence from my 'bath' in the Danube; 'comfortable' prisons; several long years of living mostly behind closed doors; a damp, cold hole under a floor—what else would one need to develop tuberculosis? It was told my case was a pretty bad one, and I needed prompt treatment. This was a time when TB was a very serious and dangerous illness, and often it ended in death. The most common cure that the doctors experienced in that hospital was air pumped under one's lungs in order to force it to stop working. No streptomicin or PAS pills were available at that time.

Lisa was the one who, again,suffered the most. After receiving new ID cards, our life began to be a little brighter; the danger of prison and death seemed to be farther and farther away; and now, suddenly, this misfortune ... Lisa, as in the past, didn't cry or show any despair. On the contrary, she tried her best to raise my spirits. I tried to respond, encouragingly, but we both knew we were acting the part.

The doctor sent me immediately to Vinogradska Bolnica Hospital in Zagreb. My ward in the hospital was a very big one with about twenty beds. All of the patients were TB victims; some in early stages; some very serious. In the corner of the room were curtained beds with hopeless cases. The men around me coughed continually. The doctors and nurses came in periodically giving some patients the necessary air. It was the second time I was in a hospital, but now I felt hopeless. "This time you will not escape your fate, Sergei," I said to myself. "You cannot run away from this sickness as you ran from prisons. The only thing you can do now is pray." And I prayed.

The foolish idea that I would die here in the hospital never left my mind. It was with me constantly and I couldn't stand it any longer. I knew it was a crazy thing to think. I couldn't even explain it to myself, but I simply felt I had to leave this place and go home.

Lisa didn't object to my decision at all, it seemed she was almost glad to hear it. But, the doctor ...

"You are doing a very stupid thing, young man," he said to me, looking at my X-ray. "You have a cavern in your lung as big as a walnut. Without treatment you will have no lung at all, say, in twelve months."

He looked at me. I didn't say anything.

"You know there are many people, sick people, who would be glad to be in here, but we have no room for them. You were lucky being accepted here so quickly. You know the hospital rules—if you leave against our advice you cannot be admitted here again." The doctor tried his last weapon.

It was all in vain—I left the hospital the same day. As I left the building I felt a heavy load lifted from me. "I will have my lung in twelve months, don't worry," I murmured, looking at the doctor's window.

According to the knowledge known then, there were three things that could help cure tuberculosis—fresh mountain air, rest and plenty of food. I was lucky again—around Samobor there were high mountains, covered with dense fir forests, something just for me. We rented a small room in a lovely house located at the edge of the forest, almost at the top of the hill. The quiet beautiful place with a wonderful view of the town, surrounded by mountains, was a pleasant change after my hospital room; I felt self-confidence and faith in the future beginning to return to me. "I will get well again," I said to myself, "in spite of any doctor's prophecy. I did not escape from Russia to die here in Samobor. I must recover, I must and I will."

The most important thing to fight TB was to gain weight. That meant to eat plenty of caloric food, as much as possible. It is not a very easy thing to do, especially when one is already full, but I forced myself to do it. I would eat all day, lying in my bed, walking in the forest, reading a book, or playing chess with myself. All our money was going for food and still there would not have been enough without Lisa's mother's parcel of food.

Several months passed and we began to see significant progress in my health. My cough stopped almost completely. I gained weight and my temperature was always normal. At the end of six months, I visited my doctor in Samobor, who was more than surprised after seeing my X-ray. "If I hadn't seen you myself a half year ago, I wouldn't believe it. Your cavern has not only stopped growing, it has begun to lime up. Without any medical treatment, this happens very, very seldom. I hope your improvement continues. Maybe you will even recover completely. I am saying maybe. Anyway, go on your way. And don't forget to visit me once a month."

We went our way, and twelve months later, one beautiful day, the doctor handed me a paper with the words, "Able to Work" stamped across it.

LXIX

During my illness I had much time which I utilized by studying accounting and bookkeeping systems in business. As a result of this study, I was accepted in a factory in the position of junior accountant. The salary was much better than I had before and the prospects for advancement were very excellent. Lisa was working in the same place, and in a couple of years we succeeded in saving enough money for a long-awaited trip to the sea.

Of course there were no more problems with our traveling because of my now perfect ID card. The vacation was unforgettable; quiet, clear sea, blue sky and warm, pleasant weather. I never saw anything so beautiful before. We wanted very much to go there every year, but our income wouldn't allow it more often than every two or three years.

As the time passed, we continued to act out our roles as ordinary Yugoslav citizens. A rule was established between Lisa and me: speak about our past only if it was absolutely necessary, even to each other. We wanted to forget everything that could bring frightful memories back to us. However, the fear was always there, even unspoken.

Life went along. I enrolled in the accounting school and advanced rapidly on my job to the position of Chief of Accounting Department. We rented a larger apartment in the same house where we were living, and Lisa was very happy to have again her own furniture and her own kitchen. She was still working. In Yugoslavia one salary wasn't enough to live on, even if it was one of Chief or Director.

From time to time Colonel Sokolov would send me news of my mother. I was happy to hear she went back to Leningrad, but there was also very sad news. My brother, Aleksey, lost his life during the war, and my mother never let me know about it, until now. She would have rather stayed alone, as she was, than to restrict my decisions of freedom. Lisa's mother visited us a couple of times, coming a long way from Subotica, and was very happy to see us living a normal life. Everything was fine at home, no more questions or searches. Surely, I was completely forgotten after so many years. Lisa's mother explained, "I believe there is no more danger for you, Sergei. You and Lisa may live very nicely here like all other young couples ... "

Obviously, she was trying to tell me something.

"Like other couples? We are living like other couples, Mother!" I didn't quite know what she meant.

"Yes, you are, but they have children. Why won't you have a baby, Sergei?"

"A baby?" I repeated, surprised.

"Yes, a baby. Don't you think it's about time? Everything is all right now. You don't need to delay any longer. What do you think, Lisa?"

"I would like very much to have a baby," Lisa said, heaving a sigh. "But I always felt we shouldn't have a baby. We are escaping, running all the time. Who knows? Maybe tomorrow we must run again ... "

"Oh, this way you'll never have your baby, Lisa!" Mother said, very upset. "You will postpone it year after year, until it will be too late. Don't you like children, Sergei?" she turned to me, warlike.

"You forget about the name, Mother." Lisa hurried to help me. "The baby would be baptized as Mezei, not as Sazonov."

"And what's wrong with Mezei? Are you trying to tell me this is your reason for not having a baby?"

"Mother, please understand. Of course, we would like to have a child, but give us some time to think it over. During all these years there wasn't any possibility even to think about having a baby. You know that yourself! But now ... why not, Lisa? We can have a baby. Maybe after a few years there will be less investigation on the issue of passports, and we could go abroad to Italy like tourists, and never return here. Then we will have our real name again," I finished, while Mother smiled approvingly.

"Will we stay in Italy, Ivan?" Lisa asked me.

"Oh, no. From Italy we are going to emigrate to America. I think the U.S.A. today is the only country where we can live in safety. I believe the Communists will never succeed in destroying Democracy in that country. There we will find our true home, and we will never have a need to run anywhere again."

LXX

In the spring of 1956, I became a happy father of a healthy strong boy. Sitting by Lisa's bed I looked at my son and could not believe it was a reality.

"He is just like you," Lisa whispered joyously. "We will call him Sergei. I always loved that name, but I could use it very, very seldom. Now I may use it any time. You mustn't forget though, his name is Sergei, not yours."

Several years passed without any changes. My son grew big and strong. We went to the sea on our vacation, periodically, enjoying the life and freedom. The whole situation in Yugoslavia became better and better, as Tito's regime was more democratic than the Russian example. Of course, it was still a Communistic country, but in comparison with Russia, one could call it paradise. The people could go abroad much easer than ever before. I had already decided to apply for our tourists visas, when something happened that destroyed all our illusive plans.

Arriving at our home the day we returned from our vacation, a strange feeling came over me as I opened the door and stepped into our apartment. "Wait a moment," I warned, stopping Lisa at the door and looking around, suspiciously. Everything seemed to be in order, chairs, tables, even the books were in their usual places, but I knew something was wrong. But what? What?

I checked the windows; they were closed as usual. I walked through all the rooms, inspected the kitchen and came back to the entrance door. Then I realized what was wrong. "Lisa, do you remember what you told me when we went away, the very last thing?"

"Well, yes, nothing special. Just the usual things. Turn off the lights. Check the windows. See that the cat is not inside ... "

"But what else? Here by the door?"

"Oh, yes. I know. Don't forget to turn the key twice ... "

"Right, and I know for sure that I did turn it twice."

We always did it, as our door couldn't be locked until the key was turned twice.

"Lisa, I opened the door with only one turn of the key. That's what gave me the strange feeling that something is wrong."

"Do you think ... ?" Lisa didn't dare finish.

"Yes, I am sure we had some visitors during our absence. Very cautious visitors, who tried, and almost succeeded, not to leave any traces after them. I am afraid, Lisa, the U.D.B.A.* discovered something about me. They probably don't know who I really am, and they will keep us under surveillance for some time."

"You're right, Ivan," Lisa said suddenly. "Look at this pillow. Do you see where I have sewn up this small hole? I always hide it by turning the pillow upsidedown. Now, you see, it is here, on this side."

"What will we do now, Ivan?" Lisa looked outside where our son played with other children.

"Nothing, darling, just wait. We cannot go anywhere now. They will follow my every move. Let's live as though nothing happened. They must believe we don't suspect anything. If I run and they capture me, it would be a point against me, proof that I am guilty of something. Anyway, it is a different situation now than it was before. They will find only the best records about my life here."

We knew we must prepare ourselves for arrest and investigation. It was very important to give the right answers to every possible question, particularly our motives and intentions. Once more we went through our whole lives, trying to memorize what we should and shouldn't say to U.D.B.A.

---

*Changed from O.Z.N.A.

LXXI

It was a day the same as any other day when I came out of my office to go home. It all happened very quickly. Two plainclothes U.D.B.A. men stopped me outside, showed me their papers, and forced me into a car. In a very short time we arrived at Zagreb. A few minutes later I was again in a cell in the investigation department of U.D.B.A.

All I could think of was Lisa and our little son. What will happen to them if I am extradited to Russia? How long will I be here? How will I be sentenced? How many years of prison awaited me? I knew the Yugoslav laws and knew they could imprison me for five years just for using a false ID card. After that they could send me to Russia. What will happen to Lisa? Will they imprison her too? And our little son!

I knew the answers to all these questions depended upon my behavior and upon my answers at the time of the investigation. Thank God, I was not called until the next morning, so I had the whole night to think. Of course, Lisa and I were ready for my eventual arrest and we knew what we would say and what we would not say, but it was impossible to know everything that would come up during the interrogation. I hoped Lisa would not be confused and say anything we dared not let them know. I hoped our 'paprika' letters would help us again.

In the morning I was there again, standing in front of U.D.B.A. officers. Outwardly I was completely composed, but inside ... I knew I could not let them notice, or they would think I was afraid and, consequently, guilty.

In a quiet voice I realted my story. Of course, I did not mention my political views. I tried to explain my case very simply: "I fell in love with a girl and married her and for that reason I remained in Yugoslavia. I would like to remain legally but O.Z.N.A. wanted to extradite me to Russia, so I was forced to remain here illegally after escaping from prison. I have a very good position as chief of accounting department and I would like to remain here." I did not say one word about Colonel Sokolov and my intention to go to U.S.A. I expressed my satisfaction with life in Yugoslavia because it was so like life in Russia, even much better than Russia. It was very important that they did not get the idea there were other reasons for my escaping from the Army, excepting my love for Lisa. I had no idea whether they were going to believe me or not, especially when I noticed some documents on the desk of the chief investigator, marked 'Subotica.' I knew then that they had my history from years back, but they had purposely left me free so they could watch my every step.

This quizzing continued for several weeks. I had to relate my story many times with more and more details, and I saw they did not believe me.

Our paprika mail functioned very well. Lisa wrote that she was free but had had several long examinations in the U.D.B.A. and I knew that she told the same story as I did. She wrote also that her family and our friends in Subotica had been questioned, too.

After about two months I was called to the interrogation office again and was confronted with three U.D.B.A. men. I felt this interview would be very important and perhaps my future would depend on the outcome. I had to tell my story again from the beginning. The officers interrupted me several times with questions, trying to confuse me. After a long time, or so it seemed to me, one of them remarked, "Well, we've heard your story again. It may be the truth, but not likely. One thing isn't clear. Why didn't you come and tell us all about it, when you first came to Samobor?"

"I was afraid you would send me to Russia."

"Yes, but after 1948 we were in very bad relations with Russia, everybody knew this very well, and you could be sure that we would not return you. Why didn't you come here voluntarily sometime after 1948?"

"Yes, it is true that I could have come here after 1948, thinking you would not extradite me; but who could guarantee that later Yugoslavia and Russia would not make up their differences? You know yourself that today Yugoslavia again is on good relations with Russia. Time has shown that I was right in not coming to you then ..."

The officers were silent; what I said was true. But after a moment, "You told lies to our men in Subotica and in Belgrade. Who could believe you now?"

"All right, but you know why I had to lie before. It was to save my wife and her family from prison. Now you know all about us. Why would I have to lie to you at this time?"

"Yes, you are a big liar. We know it. You work here for a certain spy organization and we will prove it for sure."

"Excuse me, Comrade, but if you thought I was an imperialistic spy, why did you arrest me? Why didn't you leave me at liberty and watch me, later catching the whole spy net?"

They looked at each other. "All right," one of them said, with a 'pleasant' smile, "can you explain to us again why you didn't return to Russia? Yes, we know you fell in love with your wife, but why didn't you take your wife to Russia with you, as many of your men who married here have done? Why have you remained here when you could go back to your home country?"

"Yes, I could have gone back, but my wife didn't want to leave her family and her widowed mother. She said if I loved her, I would stay here with her."

"But, you and she both knew how dangerous it would be."

"Yes, we knew it, but we were both very young and didn't understand how serious it could be. She simply didn't want to go to Russia and leave her family," I said, but inwardly I was praying, "God," I thought, "when will this end?"

"You lie. Your wife told us that **you** were the one who didn't want to go to Russia, not she. Tell us now why didn't you go back when she wasn't against it?"

"It isn't true. She couldn't say that."

"But she said it and we will show you her written statement."

"I don't believe it."

"You will see it tomorrow and then we will talk about something else. Take him away."

I returned to my cell, and, as it was nearly time for Lisa to bring my food, I hurriedly wrote her a letter.

"Lisa, darling, they will quiz you again tomorrow, saying that I said I did not want to go back to Russia, but that you were willing. Don't believe it. You must always say that **you** refused to go and forced me to stay here, if I loved you."

I had her answer the next day. "They said everything you wrote me. They shouted at me and wanted me to sign a paper that you didn't want to go back and showed me a paper with **your** signature stating that you didn't want to return to Russia, but I said to them again and again that it wasn't true. Did I help you, my darling?"

My poor brave Lisa. She not only helped me, she saved me, herself and our son.

In a few days I was set free to await trial. Eventually the U.D.B.A would have to accept my story since they couldn't prove anything else, especially anything political. However, I was obliged to report to the police every day.

My trial was set for September 6, 1961. The entire legal proceedings were quite different from the situation at the trial in Subotica fourteen years ago. I even had a defender, a lawyer from Zagreb. There wasn't a jury like in the Western countries, only two so-called "Judges-Jurors" who sat on each side of the Chief-Judge. A prosecutor from Zagreb represented the bill of indictment. According to this bill I was charged with using false documents for the purpose of hiding.

The fact that I was released from the U.D.B.A. gave me a certain hope that I might receive a rather mild judgment. Indeed, I got only ten months on probation, and no word about my extradition was mentioned in my sentence. However, the U.D.B.A. made it clear to me that they could send me back to Russia at any moment. I didn't receive any new identity documents and my permit to stay in Yugoslavia had to be renewed once every month.

I knew that my legal position in Yugoslavia was very unsafe and depended completely on the mercy of U.D.B.A. In the case of renewed friendship between Russia and Yugoslavia I could lose my head very easily. I was aware that we must leave Yugoslavia, the sooner the better.

LXXII

My first step was to try to legalize my marriage with Lisa by civil law. I applied for a license at the City of Samobor. However, the city clerks refused to give me one. According to the marriage law we could not be married without my identity document.

Fearing the worst, I went to the police and asked them to issue me an ID card, explaining why I needed it.

"Yes, why not?" they said very cordially. "We will give you your ID card, but you must fill out these forms first. You may take them home and return them to us."

I looked the forms over carefully at home, and found they were an application for Yugoslavian citizenship! I knew what it could mean to us. I would receive the ID card and Yugoslavian citizenship, and we could be married, but as soon as I became a citizen they could refuse us the right to leave the country. In addition, they could always revoke the citizenship, and then send me back to Russia. Of course, I didn't sign the forms, but Lisa and I couldn't be married.

In the meantime, I went to Belgrade, to the American Embassy and applied for immigration to the United States. I was informed that we would be permitted to immigrate, but would have to wait for the quota. They had no way of knowing how long we would have to wait. I was given forms to fill out and required to supply certain documents, among them being our marriage certificate. I explained that the Yugoslav police refused us a marriage license. One of the Embassy's counselors gave me the name of a Zagreb official to whom I was supposed to explain my problem. After a week, I was advised that we could be married without the ID card. I had no idea how this was managed, but I was so elated that I didn't bother to ask. So we were married by law, after more than a year of fighting with the Yugoslav bureaucracy.

However, in order to get visas to the United States, we had

to also have a Yugoslav visa to leave the country. When I asked for it, the U.D.B.A. gave it to me as to an alien, but refused to give one for Lisa and our son. They knew that I would not go without my family! I realized I had to find some other way to solve this new problem.

After our marriage, Lisa did not change her ID card for a new one with my name on it. Utilizing this, she applied for visas for herself and our son to West Germany to visit her sister. Luckily the Visa Department at the police didn't realize that Lisa Mezei was, in fact, Lisa Sazonov. She got the visas the same way as other people got them as a matter of routine.

With Lisa's and the child's visas in hand our main troubles were solved. We planned that Lisa and our son would go immediately to West Germany and wait there for me. As soon as I received the visas for United States, I would go to Germany and we would continue together to United States.

I was very happy when I received the letter from Germany telling me they were safe. Now, I only had to wait for my visa and we would go to the United States together, whether the U.D.B.A. wished it or not. But, it wasn't as simple as I thought. I was told at the American Embassy to expect the visa in a very short time. But the time passed and my visa did not come. My attempts to hasten it at the Embassy had not succeeded. I simply had to wait my turn. In the meantime, Lisa's time on her visitor's visa had elapsed, but she did not return to Yugoslavia. Of course, the police discovered right away that it was my wife who left the country under her maiden name. I could imagine their surprise, but I was worried about what they intended to do with me.

When I went to the police station as usual to extend my temporary permit, I was called into an office where I had to face a U.D.B.A. officer who looked me up and down and took his time speaking to me. I stood there, expecting the worst.

"Your wife," he began to speak, "our citizen, remained in West Germany without our permission, and she got there only because there was an error in our office. Of course, she did it with your permission, or more exactly because of your permission. We will give you your temporary month's permit as usual, but we insist your wife come back in that time. If she refuses to return, we will not grant you another month's temporary stay in Yugoslavia and will extradite you to Russia. That is all."

I knew then that I had to escape from Yugoslavia, no matter what the cost. I asked the American Embassy once more for the visa, but it did not come. I looked for some way to get away but it seemed all ways of escape were closed. I had no choice, other than to run the risk of sneaking across the border at night as I had done years before.

LXXIII

As I was making my plans, I received a letter from Lisa telling me to go to a certain address in Lubljana. I went, watching that no one followed me. There I met a lady who explained that her relatives, a couple with a child, went to West Germany and remained there, just as Lisa did. Here, in Yugoslavia they left their other child, an eight year old daughter, Vishnja. The authorities, now, wouldn't permit the little girl to go to her parents.

"If you will take the little girl to West Germany, I can give you the address of my relative who lives near the Austria border and he will help you get across. You will have to travel all across Austria, then cross the Austria-West Germany border, then reach Nurnburg where your wife and this child's parents are. Do you agree to help us, since the girl is too young to travel alone?"

"Of course I do!" I answered happily. Everything was settled and the following week little Vishnja and I got on a train in Lubljana and traveled to a little village where her uncle lived. She was a very sensible child and conducted herself very well. I felt she was just as precious to her parents as our little son was to Lisa and me. We arrived at her uncle's home without being followed. His house was some distance from the border;but located on a hill. From there we could see the border. The old man explained where and how I should go across. He drew a map for me and pointed out everything from his yard.

"With some luck and enough care, you can get across, and God be with you," he said.

Just after noon we started our trip. Maybe now, this will be the last time I will have to sneak across a border, I thought.

First we crossed a large field in a wagon belonging to a man who went to the forest every day for firewood. We lay in the wagon covered with dirty sacks. The border patrol walked by. If they had approached the wagon, they would have seen us. People from the village usually went to the forest for firewood and the patrols did not pay too much attention to them. After getting through the forest, we walked about two hours to a hill where we had to wait until midnight.

Then we climbed another hill from where we could see the border, and we waited there until morning. Early in the morning we crossed the border without any trouble, and entered Austria. Compared with my past experiences, this crossing seemed like the easiest one. After about three hours of walking, we found a railway station, where I bought tickets for Salzburg, using money the old uncle had given me for this purpose. It all took place just exactly as the old uncle had said it would. I carried the little girl part of the way, and thanked God for the privilege. It seemed I was carrying my own little child and her slight weight was a blessing. She fell asleep, while we waited on top of the hill, but she did not cry when I waked her after midnight. Crossing the forest and sitting on the hill I felt I was again at the front in Ukraine, or Rumania. But, no, it was 1963, not 1943, and the voices and footsteps I heard in the darkness were not the enemy's, they were the border guards and sleeping here were not my soldiers, but a little girl, not more than a baby, who wanted to be with her mother.

It was a very beautiful autumn morning, November 1, 1963, when we, Vishnja and I, walked along the road to the railway station, "Speilfeld." It was a very nice name and very nice people were around: "Eine und half nach Salsburg, bitte!"* On the train to Salzburg we traveled as other free people, like father and daughter. I heaved a sigh of relief, thinking that I never again would have to be afraid of the red stars on the caps of a Yugoslav uniform. And what a wonderful thing to be a really free man!

We arrived in Salzburg, but we had one last obstruction, the Austria-West Germany border. "That will be child's play for us old, illegal people, won't it, Vishnja?" I asked the child.

"Yes, Dad," she answered laughing.

"What did your uncle say to do now?"

"Taxi!" she answered quickly, and we found a taxi, which took us to the border.

"Aufwiederseen,"** I said to the driver when I noticed the big

---

*One and a half fares to Salzburg, please.

**Good night.

lights of the border station.

On the right of the road and slightly forward was a little brook just as I had been told. "Carry my shoes," I said to the little one and I waded across the brook with her in my arms.

"Look, Vishnja, here is Germany. Let's give three cheers. Now another little walk to the railway station and everything will be all right."

We reached Bad Reichenhall. "Eine und half nach Nurnburg, bitte!"*

On the morning of November second we arrived in Nurnburg where our families waited for us. I can never describe the joyous meeting of Vishnja and her parents, who felt so uncertain about my getting through with her. But Lisa knew. She "just knew" that I would make it.

There were much happiness, tears, laughter and talk. The dangers were all past, far in the distance, and we could at last really hope that we would get to America.

Little Vishnja and her family left soon for Australia where they live today.

We had to wait nearly a year before our documents came to Muchen's U.S. consulate from Belgrade with our quota numbers. The day we received our visas for the United States will never be forgotten. We held the papers in our hand, but could not believe it was true that it was possible that we had won our fight for freedom. We thanked God, who was with us always, just as Mother had told me years before. He had helped us in our most difficult moments. He had heard our prayers and He kept our marriage as we knew He would there before the crucifix in the little church in Subotica.

---

*One and a half fares to Nurnburg, please.

EPILOGUE

We arrived in the United States in September, 1964. Exactly twenty years before, in a small Hungarian town, I held in my hands a Bible. I didn't know then that I was standing at the beginning of a long, thorny way, holding in my hands the guide to my spiritual and physical liberty. This road was a long twenty years. This was the road where I found my faith, my love and, in the end, my freedom.

After settling in California, I am today Chief Accountant for a corporation.

I attended evening school for foreign students. Then I enrolled in an adult high school. This year I graduated, and now I am going to college.

A very sad event happened to me and my family last year. I received word that my mother died in Leningrad. I always had a ray of hope that we would be re-united once again. My hopes were never realized. She knew better than I when she said, "I'll never see you again."

I began to write this book immediately after arriving in the United States. Of course, it was a very tremendous task, because of my inadequate knowledge of English. I am expressing my deep gratitude to everyone who helped me with my work.

In several cases, in order to protect the innocent, I had to change some names, places and dates. However, the events remained unchanged.

In my book I have not uncovered any political secrets, or any famous names in the Communistic Hierarchy. I wasn't one with a high position, or one who took part in making the laws, or one who forced them into life. I was one of the nameless millions who were forced to endure those laws. But I believe this book can help in the life-or-death struggle between Democratic Word and International Communism.

It will soon be five years that I have been in the United States.

As every alien resident here, I have my ID card; of course—a real one this time. I must carry it with me always for identification purposes. However, during all these years nobody has ever asked me to prove my identity.

A strange country, this America.